# Contents

# How to Use this Book

*Super Sleuth* is a unique mathematical problem-solving series for 1st to 6th Class primary school pupils. Problem-solving requires pupils to understand and explore a problem, find a strategy, use the strategy to solve the problem and look back and reflect on the solution. *Super Sleuth* focuses on the process of problem-solving and the development of the **ten main problem-solving strategies**. The series has **regular built-in revision** units, which consolidate problem-solving skills.

## Differentiation   

Differentiation is catered for in each unit through the use of **bronze**, **silver** and **gold** medals that indicate the level of difficulty and provide an entry point for every pupil as well as opportunities for **high-achievers** to be challenged.

## Collaborative learning

**The series facilitates collaborative learning** through **whole-class**, **pair** and **group work** activities. This creates an ideal classroom environment for pupils to develop their maths language and thinking, in which the teacher can act as facilitator and every pupil's contribution is valued. Learning can be applied at home through practice.

## Dedicated strategy units 

Each book dedicates **five units to a specific strategy** and pupils are encouraged to utilise and apply the strategies where relevant.

## Super Sleuth's ten problem-solving strategies:

- Trial and improvement
- Working backwards
- Working systematically
- Logical reasoning
- Visualising/Draw a picture

- Identifying patterns
- Make a table
- Act it out
- Make a model
- Simplifying

## CLUES

CLUES is a teacher- and pupil-friendly **framework** developed uniquely for *Super Sleuth* to tackle the most common **problem-solving difficulties** experienced in the classroom. It was created in order to promote Bloom's higher forms of thinking in maths education.

Miss Carroll went to the art shop to buy a set of 28 small aprons and a set of 28 large aprons. How many aprons did she buy?

**C**ircle the numbers and keywords: 28, 28, how many?

**L**ink with operation needed (+ or –): Add (+).

**U**se a strategy: Draw a picture.

**E**stimate and calculate:

My estimate: more than 40

| | T | U |
|---|---|---|
| | 2 | 8 |
| + | 2 | 8 |
| | 5 | 6 |

**Answer:** 56

**S**ummarise how you got your answer: I added 2 groups of 28.

# Super Sleuth key features

**Weekly structure:** Weekly arrangement of work (30 units) and provides four days of work with three to four questions per day.

**WALT:** Clear learning outcomes are provided at the beginning of each new strand.

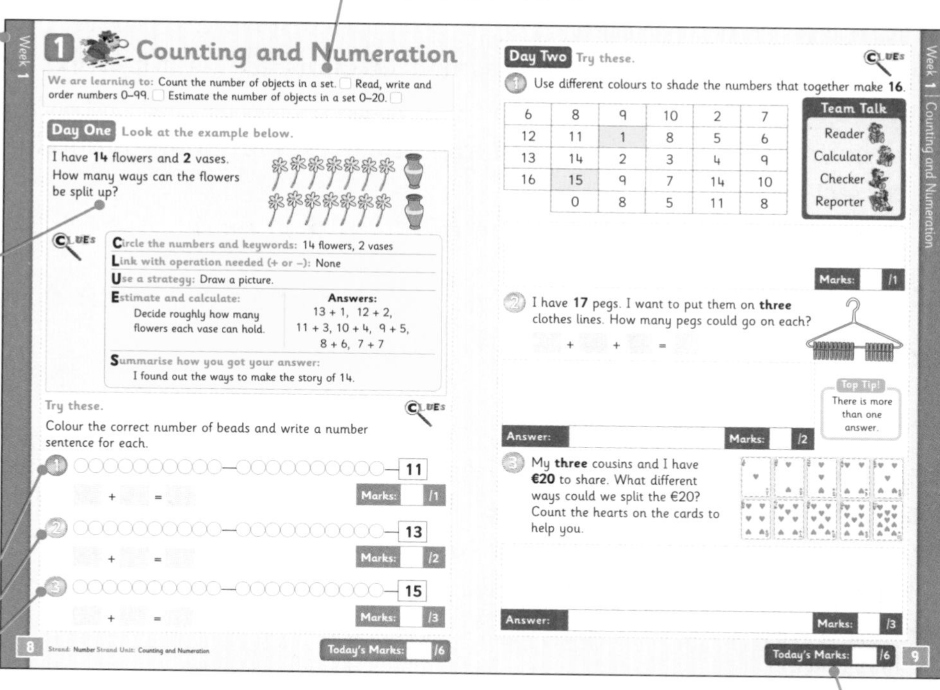
Week 1

## 1 Counting and Numeration

We are learning to: Count the number of objects in a set. ☐ Read, write and order numbers 0–99. ☐ Estimate the number of objects in a set 0–20. ☐

**Day One** Look at the example below.

I have **14** flowers and **2** vases. How many ways can the flowers be split up?

**C**ircle the numbers and keywords: 14 flowers, 2 vases
**L**ink with operation needed (+ or –): None
**U**se a strategy: Draw a picture.
**E**stimate and calculate: Decide roughly how many flowers each vase can hold. **Answers:** 13 + 1, 12 + 2, 11 + 3, 10 + 4, 9 + 5, 8 + 6, 7 + 7
**S**ummarise how you got your answer: I found out the ways to make the story of 14.

Try these.
Colour the correct number of beads and write a number sentence for each.

1. 11 — + = — Marks: /1
2. 13 — + = — Marks: /2
3. 15 — + = — Marks: /3

8 Strand: Number Strand Unit: Counting and Numeration — Today's Marks: /6

**Day Two** Try these.

1. Use different colours to shade the numbers that together make **16**.

| 6 | 8 | 9 | 10 | 2 | 7 |
|---|---|---|---|---|---|
| 12 | 11 | 1 | 8 | 5 | 6 |
| 13 | 14 | 2 | 3 | 4 | 9 |
| 16 | 15 | 9 | 7 | 14 | 10 |
| | 0 | 8 | 5 | 11 | 8 |

Team Talk: Reader, Calculator, Checker, Reporter

Marks: /1

2. I have **17** pegs. I want to put them on **three** clothes lines. How many pegs could go on each? + + =

Top Tip! There is more than one answer.

Answer: Marks: /2

3. My **three** cousins and I have **€20** to share. What different ways could we split the €20? Count the hearts on the cards to help you.

Answer: Marks: /3

Today's Marks: /6 9

Week 1 | Counting and Numeration

**Worked example:** A worked example using the CLUES framework is provided at the start of new strands to demonstrate a strategy that pupils can follow, allowing them to work independently.

**Clear differentiation:** Each page is differentiated using bronze, silver and gold medals to show the level of difficulty and give pupils an incentive to progress. The bronze medal indicates a question that the majority of the class should work on independently. The silver medal poses more of a challenge, while the gold medal may require collaborative work in order for the pupils to reach a solution.

**Progress recording:** Each question and week has a score tracker to help pupils self-assess.

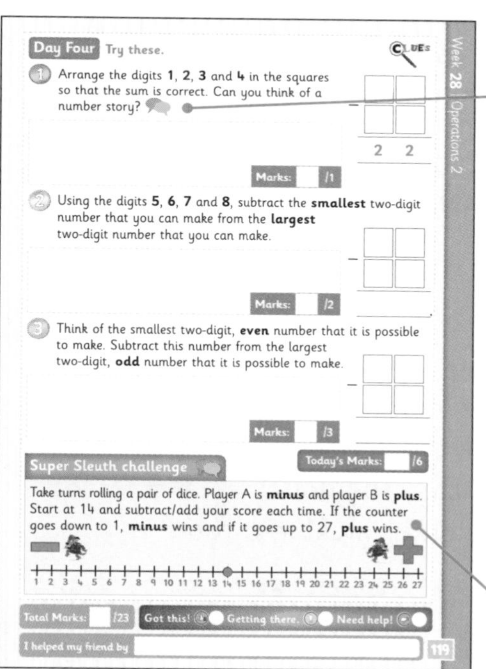
**Day Four** Try these.

1. Arrange the digits **1**, **2**, **3** and **4** in the squares so that the sum is correct. Can you think of a number story? (– 2 2) Marks: /1
2. Using the digits **5**, **6**, **7** and **8**, subtract the **smallest** two-digit number that you can make from the **largest** two-digit number that you can make. Marks: /2
3. Think of the smallest two-digit, **even** number that it is possible to make. Subtract this number from the largest two-digit, **odd** number that it is possible to make. Marks: /3

Today's Marks: /6

Super Sleuth challenge

Take turns rolling a pair of dice. Player A is **minus** and player B is **plus**. Start at 14 and subtract/add your score each time. If the counter goes down to 1, **minus** wins and if it goes up to 27, **plus** wins.

1 2 3 4 5 6 7 8 9 10 11 12 13 14 15 16 17 18 19 20 21 22 23 24 25 26 27

Total Marks: /23 Got this! Getting there. Need help!

I helped my friend by

119

Week 28 Operations 2

**Pair work/group work:** Opportunities are provided for pair and group work. Group work can be applied to activities and these specific questions are highlighted throughout the book, where different roles can be assigned to up to four pupils.

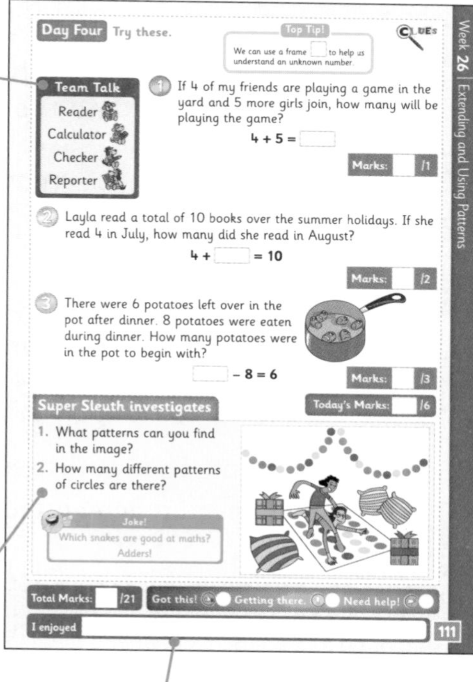
**Day Four** Try these.

Top Tip! We can use a frame ☐ to help us understand an unknown number.

Team Talk: Reader, Calculator, Checker, Reporter

1. If 4 of my friends are playing a game in the yard and 5 more girls join, how many will be playing the game? 4 + 5 = ☐ Marks: /1
2. Layla read a total of 10 books over the summer holidays. If she read 4 in July, how many did she read in August? 4 + ☐ = 10 Marks: /2
3. There were 6 potatoes left over in the pot after dinner. 8 potatoes were eaten during dinner. How many potatoes were in the pot to begin with? ☐ – 8 = 6 Marks: /3

Super Sleuth investigates — Today's Marks: /6

1. What patterns can you find in the image?
2. How many different patterns of circles are there?

Joke! Which snakes are good at maths? Adders!

Total Marks: /21 Got this! Getting there. Need help!

I enjoyed

111

Week 26 | Extending and Using Patterns

**Puzzles and challenges:** 'Super Sleuth challenge' is an open-ended question based on the maths skills and strand covered in the unit. 'Super Sleuth investigates' is an activity for applying the maths skills/strand of the unit to a situation that could be encountered in real life.

**Self-assessment:** The self-assessment section for each strand offers pupils an opportunity to reflect on their learning, as well as providing very valuable information to the teacher.

## Problem-solving strategies

### Trial and improvement

- The strategy of trial and improvement encourages pupils to make a reasonable estimate, giving them a starting point as they attempt to solve the puzzle.
- The pupils are then asked to check their estimate to see if it works as a solution and revise it accordingly.
- By repeating this process and changing their estimate appropriately, pupils should arrive at the correct answer.
- All rough work should be kept as a record of their work.

**Example:** On a farm there were some hens and cows. Altogether there were 8 heads and 22 feet. How many hens were there?

### Working backwards

- Occasionally pupils come across a puzzle in which they are given the final answer and the steps taken to arrive at the answer, but they are not given the data from the start of the puzzle. They must undo each step to get back to the starting point.
- Pupils can draw a diagram to show the known facts and use the inverse operation when working backwards.

**Example:** Martha removed a loaf of bread from the oven after it had been baking for two hours. If she took it out at 4 o'clock, at what time did she put it into the oven?

### Working systematically

- Working systematically requires pupils to work carefully through the information they are given.
- This strategy may incorporate other strategies for pupils to draw upon in order to work out the process of the problem. They might need to make a list, draw a diagram, make a table or explore problems with numerous answers in order to organise and build on the information until they find the solution.

**Example:** There are six ice-cream flavours to choose from. How many different two-scoop ice-cream cones can be made?

### Logical reasoning

- Logical reasoning can be explained as a proper or reasonable way of thinking about something. It requires the pupils to think carefully about the information they have been given and decide on a way of using the information to solve the puzzle.
- Pupils are encouraged to use a step-by-step approach to reach a solution.
- This may involve implementing a strategy such as visualisation or making a table.

**Example:** Grumpy, Sneezy, Sleepy and Doc are all in line for the cinema. Sleepy is ahead of Grumpy, Sneezy is behind Grumpy and Doc is second. What is their order from first to last?

### Visualising / Draw a picture

- Drawing a diagram can help pupils to visualise a puzzle. By doing this, they can make connections within the puzzle and plan how to solve it.
- Diagrams can include tree diagrams, timelines, pictures, symbols and Venn diagrams.

**Example:** Felix made 12 butterfly buns and iced them. He placed two chocolate buttons on top of each bun. How many chocolate buttons did he use?

### Identifying patterns

- This strategy involves pupils investigating how numbers, images or symbols are arranged in a variety of orders.
- Each pattern follows a rule. Pupils may be asked to identify the rule in a pattern, find the missing value(s) or extend the existing pattern. Many things in our world follow a set of rules, so that we know what to expect.

**Example:** Millie is making a beaded necklace that follows a pattern of red, green, blue. If she uses 18 beads in total, how many red beads will she use?

### Make a table

- When puzzles are written in word sentences, they can be confusing for pupils.
- Making a table helps pupils to organise the information that they have and identify the information that they need.

**Example:** Mikey saves €4 on Monday. Each day after that, he saves twice as much as the day before. How much money will he have saved by Friday?

### Act it out

- Acting it out is an effective strategy for pupils who have difficulty visualising a problem.
- Acting out a problem using props such as cubes or string, or in pairs or groups can greatly simplify finding solutions and is an effective strategy for demonstration purposes in front of the whole class.

**Example:** I have a 5 litre jug and a 3 litre jug. How can I measure out 7 litres of juice using these jugs?

### Make a model

- By making a model, the pupils are given an opportunity to showcase their understanding of a specific area of maths. For example, pupils can investigate the properties of 3-D shapes through model building.

**Example:** Using 26 cocktail sticks and Blu-tack, how many cubes can Emily make and how many cocktail sticks will be left over?

### Simplifying

There are three ways in which pupils can simplify a puzzle:

- Reword the puzzle using a more familiar setting.
- Break the puzzle down into steps and solve one part at a time.
- Use smaller numbers.

**Example:** Amy spent $\frac{1}{8}$ of her savings on a new jacket. If she had €320 in savings, how much did the jacket cost?

$\frac{1}{8}$ of €32 = €4 ➔ $\frac{1}{8}$ of €320 = €40

# 1 Counting and Numeration

**We are learning to:** Count the number of objects in a set. ☐ Read, write and order numbers 0–99. ☐ Estimate the number of objects in a set 0–20. ☐

## Day One Look at the example below.

I have **14** flowers and **2** vases. How many ways can the flowers be split up?

**Circle the numbers and keywords:** 14 flowers, 2 vases

**Link with operation needed (+ or –):** None

**Use a strategy:** Draw a picture.

**Estimate and calculate:**
Decide roughly how many flowers each vase can hold.

**Answers:**
13 + 1, 12 + 2, 11 + 3, 10 + 4, 9 + 5, 8 + 6, 7 + 7

**Summarise how you got your answer:**
I found out the ways to make the story of 14.

### Try these.

Colour the correct number of beads and write a number sentence for each.

1. ○○○○○○○○○○—○○○○○○○○○○— **11**

☐ + ☐ = ☐

Marks: ☐ /1

2. ○○○○○○○○○○—○○○○○○○○○○— **13**

☐ + ☐ = ☐

Marks: ☐ /2

3. ○○○○○○○○○○—○○○○○○○○○○— **15**

☐ + ☐ = ☐

Marks: ☐ /3

Today's Marks: ☐ /6

## Day Two Try these.

1. Use different colours to shade the numbers that together make **16**.

| 6 | 8 | 9 | 10 | 2 | 7 |
|---|---|---|---|---|---|
| 12 | 11 | 1 | 8 | 5 | 6 |
| 13 | 14 | 2 | 3 | 4 | 9 |
| 16 | 15 | 9 | 7 | 14 | 10 |
| | 0 | 8 | 5 | 11 | 8 |

**Team Talk**

Reader
Calculator
Checker
Reporter

**Marks:** /1

2. I have **17** pegs. I want to put them on **three** clothes lines. How many pegs could go on each?

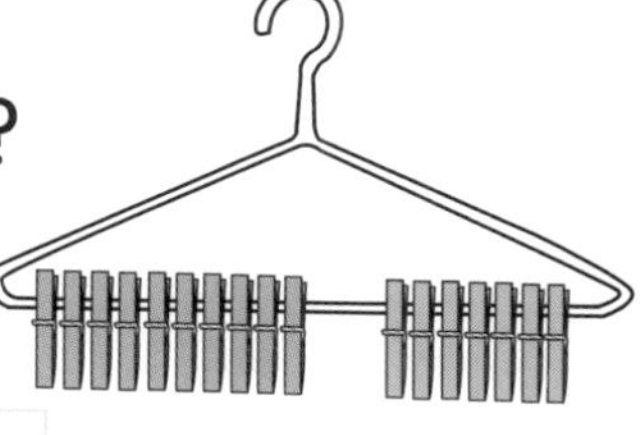

+ + =

**Top Tip!** There is more than one answer.

**Answer:** **Marks:** /2

3. My **three** cousins and I have **€20** to share. What different ways could we split the €20? Count the hearts on the cards to help you.

**Answer:** **Marks:** /3

## Day Three Try these.

1. How many pigs, horses and sheep are there on the farm?

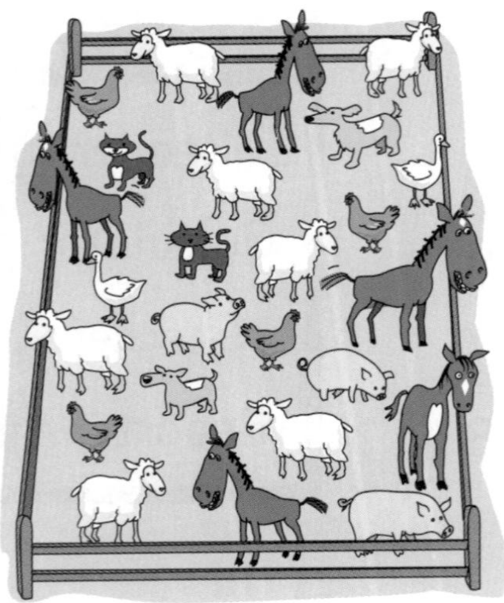

**Top Tip!**
Count each animal inside the pen.

Marks: /1

2. There are **24** pupils in 1st Class, **31** pupils in 2nd Class and **28** pupils in 3rd Class. Put the classes in order from the largest to the smallest.

Answer:

Marks: /2

3. Mag is **56** years old, Parker is **22** years old, Dot is **93** years old and Ken is **47** years old. Put them in order, starting with the oldest.

Answer:

Marks: /3

### Super Sleuth challenge

Judith picked 20 flowers in her granny's garden. Some were **red** and some were **yellow**. What numbers of each colour might she have picked?



Today's Marks: /6

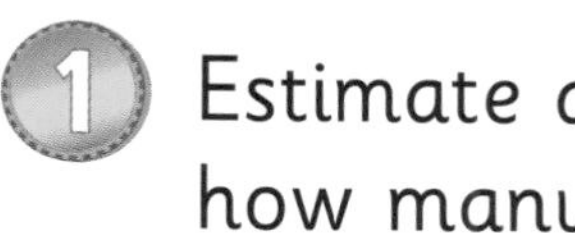

## Day Four Try these.

**Keyword**

An **estimate** is a close guess of the value.

1 Estimate and then check how many colouring pencils there are in total.

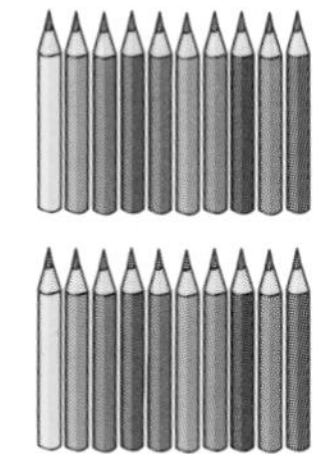
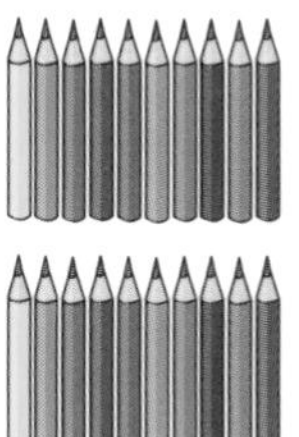

Answer: Marks: /1

2 Estimate and then check how many fish there are in total.

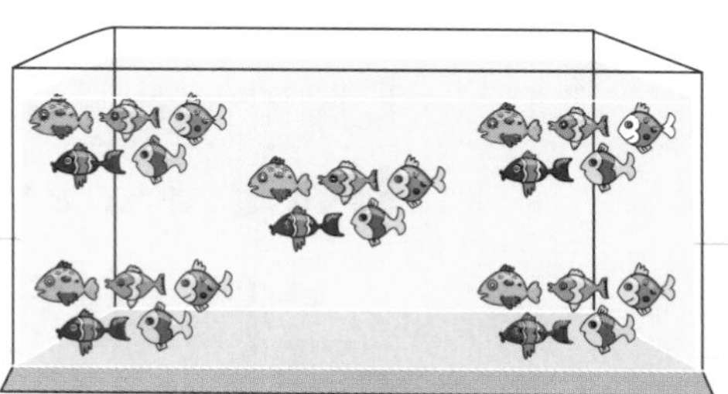

Answer: Marks: /2

3 Bob the Builder is building **100** houses. How many more does he have left to build?

Answer: Marks: /3

## Puzzle power

Today's Marks: /6

What goes around the world, but stays in the corner?

Put the numbers in order, starting with the least, to find the answer.

| 15 | 26 | 12 | 19 | 28 |
|---|---|---|---|---|
| t | m | s | a | p |

Total Marks: /24

Got this!  Getting there.  Need help! 

I would like to get better at

# 2 Comparing and Ordering

**We are learning to:** Compare groups by using the words more, few or fewer. ☐ Use the words 1st to 10th. ☐ Order groups by number. ☐

## Day One Look at the example below.

There are **6** boys and **9** girls in 1st Class. How many **more** girls than boys are there?

**C**ircle the numbers and keywords: 6 boys, 9 girls

**L**ink with operation needed (+ or –): None

**U**se a strategy:

Draw a picture.

**E**stimate and calculate:

My estimate: less than 5.
Pair up the boys and girls.

**Answer:** 3

**S**ummarise how you got your answer:

I paired them up and had 3 girls left over.

**Try these.**

1. Taylor made **3** daisy chains. Julian made **6** daisy chains. Who made the **fewest** daisy chains?

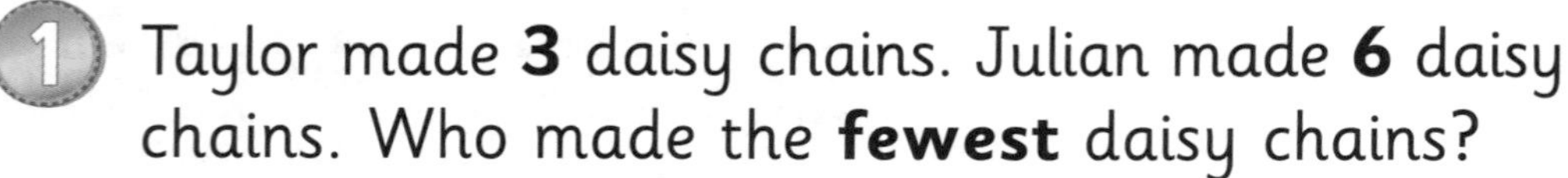

Answer:

Marks: /1

2. Camila scored **5** baskets. Isaac scored **8** baskets. How many **more** baskets did Isaac score than Camilla?

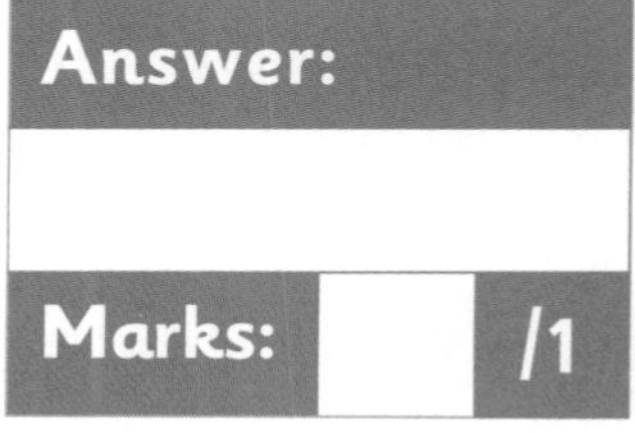

Answer:

Marks: /2

3. Eva and Rhona baked some cookies with their dad. Eva baked **12** cookies and Rhona baked **16** cookies. How many **more** cookies did Rhona bake?

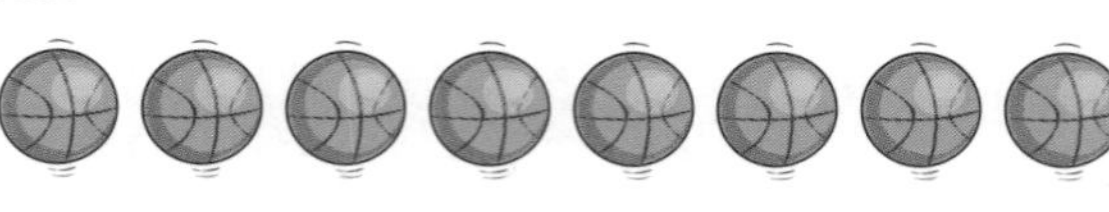

Answer:

Marks: /3



**Today's Marks:** /6

## Day Two Try these.

**Team Talk**

Reader
Calculator
Checker
Reporter

Bina and her friends played a game called 'Lowest Score Wins'. They each rolled a pair of dice and added the numbers that landed together. The aim of the game was to get the **lowest** score.

- Bina scored **12**.
- Damian scored **8**.
- Zoe scored **7**.
- Alf scored **14**.

**Top Tip!**
Act it out.

1. Who won the game?

**Answer:** **Marks:** /1

2. Who had the highest score?

**Answer:** **Marks:** /1

3. What was the difference between the two nearest scores?

**Answer:** **Marks:** /2

4. What would have been the lowest possible score?

**Answer:** **Marks:** /3

## Puzzle power

| Ring the correct answer.<br>4 comes **before** / **after** 3<br>5 comes **before** / **after** 6 | Ring the number that comes between 6 and 8.<br>**3** / **10** / **7** |
|---|---|

**Today's Marks:** /7

## Day Three  Try these.

**Keyword**

An **ordinal number** tells us the position of an item in a sequence, e.g. the 1st sleuth, the 4th sleuth. When you see the words 'ordinal number', think about **order**.

|  |  |  |  |  |  |  |  |  | |
|---|---|---|---|---|---|---|---|---|---|
| **1st** first | **2nd** second | **3rd** third | **4th** fourth | **5th** fifth | **6th** sixth | **7th** seventh | **8th** eighth | **9th** ninth | **10th** tenth |

1. Ring the correct ordinal position for each sleuth.

| | |
|---|---|
|  | 1st / 3rd / 6th |
|  | 2nd / 6th / 9th |
|  | 4th / 7th / 10th |

**Marks:** /1

**Joke!**

What has four legs and can't walk?

A chair!

2. Which sleuth came one after the 3rd sleuth?

**Answer:** **Marks:** /1

3. Carmel is **1st** in the line at the bus stop. Robin is **2nd** and Alex is next. **(a)** What position is Alex in the line? **(b)** What position is three after Alex?

**Answers:** **(a)** **(b)** **Marks:** /2

4. **(a)** What colour car is coming after the **3rd** car? **(b)** If it skipped two cars, what position would it be in then?

**Answers:** **(a)** **(b)** **Marks:** /3



**Today's Marks:** /7

## Day Four Try these.

**Team Talk**
- Reader
- Calculator
- Checker
- Reporter

1. Johanna had **19** friends at her party and **1** more joined later. How many friends came to the party altogether?

**Top Tip!** Write a number sentence.

Answer: Marks: /1

2. **15** boys were swimming in the pool. **2** got out to go on the slide. How many boys were left in the pool?

Answer: Marks: /2

3. Mammy baked **13** loaves of bread and then baked **3** more. She burned **1** and threw it out. How many loaves did she have left?

Answer: Marks: /3

Today's Marks: /6

### Puzzle power

What runs but cannot walk? Write the letters below.
The **3rd** letter is t. The **4th** letter is e. The **1st** letter is w.
The **2nd** letter is a. The **5th** letter is r.

**1st**

Total Marks: /26

Got this!  Getting there.  Need help! 

I enjoyed

# 3 Addition

**We are learning to:** Explore repeated addition. ☐ Recall mental strategies for addition facts to 20. ☐ Make number sentences and number stories. ☐

## Day One Look at the example below.

Liam gave his two dogs treats. Nala got **2** treats and Eli got **4** treats. How many treats were given altogether?

**C**ircle the numbers and keywords: 2 treats, 4 treats, altogether

**L**ink with operation needed (+ or –): Add (+).

**U**se a strategy: Draw a picture.

**E**stimate and calculate:

My estimate: less than 10

| T | U |
|---|---|
| | 2 |
| + | 4 |
| | 6 |

**Answer:** 6

**S**ummarise how you got your answer:

I added up the number of treats altogether.

**Try these.**

1. Cara has **4** hair slides and Poppy has **5** hair slides. How many hair slides do they have altogether?

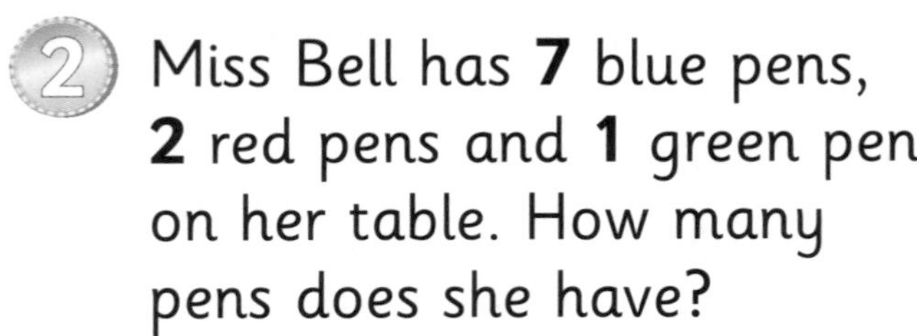

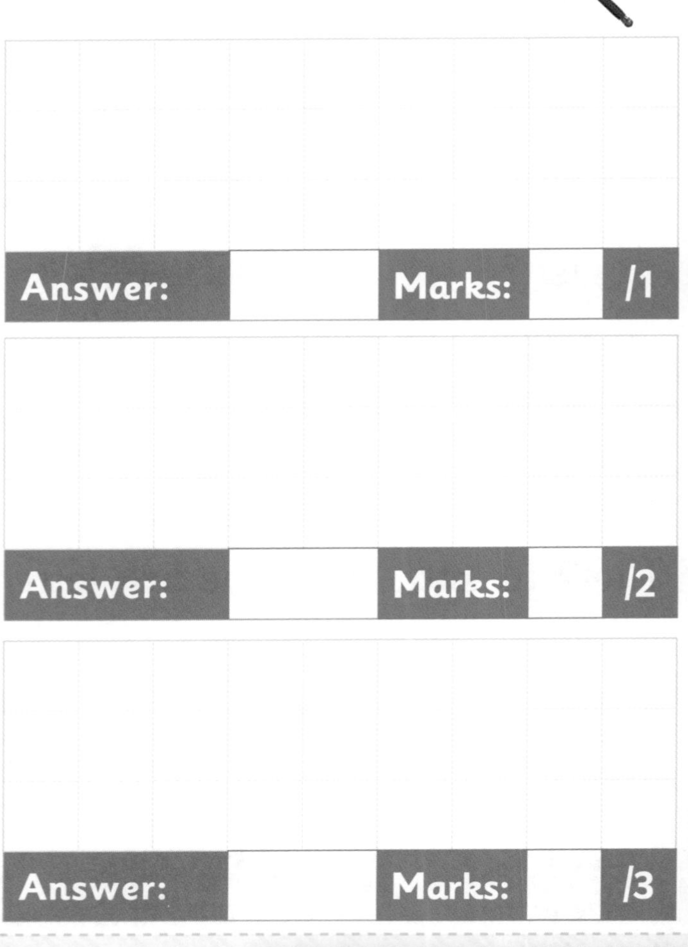

Answer: ___ Marks: ___ /1

2. Miss Bell has **7** blue pens, **2** red pens and **1** green pen on her table. How many pens does she have?

Answer: ___ Marks: ___ /2

3. At the beach, Jonah collected **8** shells, **7** rocks and **4** pebbles. How many items did he collect?

Answer: ___ Marks: ___ /3



Today's Marks: ___ /6

## Day Two Try these.

1. Add the number of ugly sisters in 'Cinderella' together with the number of elves in 'The Elves and the Shoemaker'.

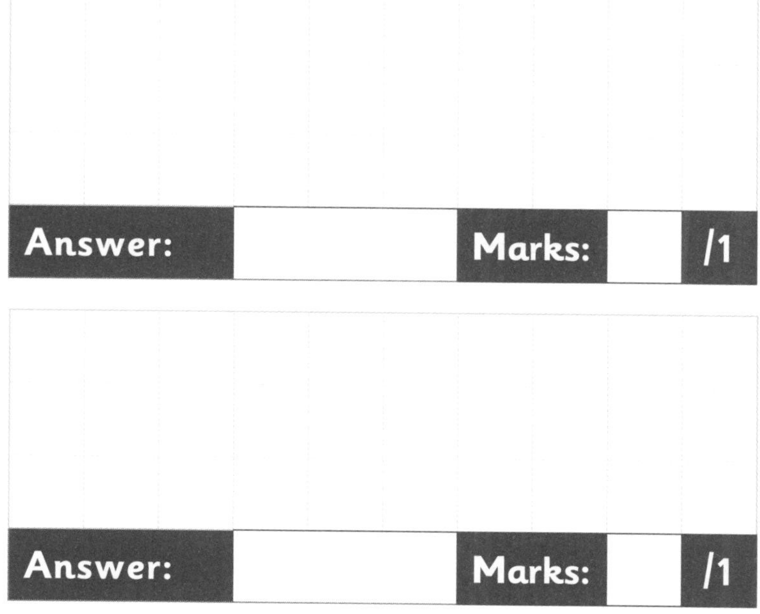

| Answer: | | Marks: | | /1 |
|---|---|---|---|---|

2. Add the number of pigs in 'The Three Little Pigs' together with the number of dwarfs in 'Snow White and the Seven Dwarfs'.

| Answer: | | Marks: | | /1 |
|---|---|---|---|---|

**Top Tip!**

3 + 6 =

It is easier to add 6 + 3 than 3 + 6.
Start with the larger number and count on.

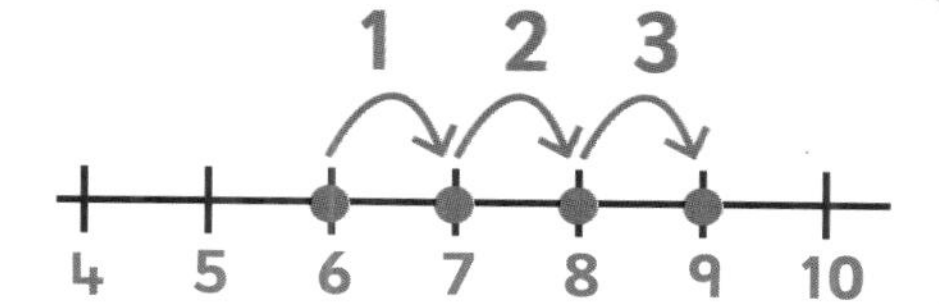


3. In 'Jack and the Beanstalk', the hen laid **7** golden eggs every morning. How many eggs did it lay in **two** mornings?

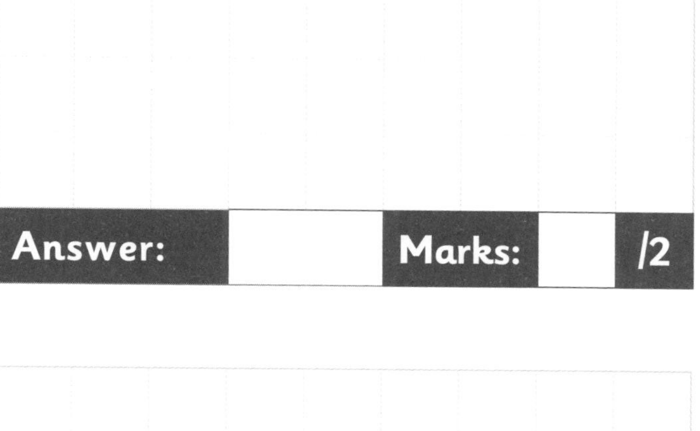

| Answer: | | Marks: | | /2 |
|---|---|---|---|---|

4. Little Red Riding Hood had **4** eggs, **1** cake and **8** cookies in her basket. How many items were in her basket altogether?

| Answer: | | Marks: | | /3 |
|---|---|---|---|---|

### Puzzle power

I am an odd number. I have one digit. I am more than 5. I am less than 8. What number am I?

**Today's Marks:** /7

## Day Three Try these.

**Top Tip!** We can use brackets to make it easier to add three or more numbers in a number sentence. Add the numbers in brackets first.

$2 + 1 + 5 =$
$(2 + 1) + 5 =$
$3 + 5 = 8$

Write a number sentence for each of the maths stories below.

1. Amy had **1** scoop of ice-cream, Tom had **2** scoops of ice-cream and Lisa had **3** scoops of ice-cream. How many scoops of ice-cream did they have altogether?

**Answer:** Marks: /1

2. Miss Collins bought **3** plain cones, **12** cones with a flake and **5** cones with strawberry syrup. How many cones did she buy in total?

**Answer:** Marks: /2

3. At the end of a busy day, the ice-cream van had only **7** cones, **8** flakes and **2** bananas left over. How many items were left over?

**Answer:** Marks: /3

### Super Sleuth challenge

In your copy, make up your own maths stories using the numbers from the questions above.



Today's Marks: /6

## Day Four Try these.

1. On a roller coaster, there were **6** carriages. If **two** children sat in each carriage, how many children were on the roller coaster?

**Answer:** **Marks:** /1

2. **5** people fit in a doughnut at the water park. If there are **five** doughnuts, how many people can fit?

**Answer:** **Marks:** /2

3. **10** people fit on each row of the Ripsaw ride. How many would fit on **three** rows?

**Answer:** **Marks:** /3

## Super Sleuth investigates

**Today's Marks:** /6

Look at the toy cars.

1. Why do you think they have numbers on them?
2. Add two of the car numbers to make 20.

**Total Marks:** /25 **Got this!**  **Getting there.**  **Need help!** 

**My favourite activity was**

Week 4

# 4 Data

**We are learning to:** Sort and classify objects by two and three criteria. ☐
Show and understand data in rows or columns using pictures. ☐

## Day One Look at the example below.

This pictogram shows the ways that pupils travel to school.
How many different ways do they travel to school?

| | | | | |
|---|---|---|---|---|
| 6 | | | | |
| 5 | | | | |
| 4 | | | | |
| 3 | | | | |
| 2 | | | | |
| 1 | | | | |

CLUES

**C**ircle the numbers and keywords:
different ways, travel to school

**L**ink with operation needed (+ or –): None

**U**se a strategy: Act it out.

| **E**stimate and calculate: My estimate: less than 5 | Count how many types of picture there are. | **Answer:** 4 |
|---|---|---|

**S**ummarise how you got your answer:
I counted the number of different ways to travel.

### Try these.

CLUES

Look at the pictogram above. How many pupils travel by ?

| **Answer:** | | **Marks:** | | /1 |
|---|---|---|---|---|

How many more pupils than travel by ?

| **Answer:** | | **Marks:** | | /2 |
|---|---|---|---|---|

3. If a new boy joins the class and he cycles to school, how many pupils cycle to school now?

| **Answer:** | | **Marks:** | | /3 |
|---|---|---|---|---|

**Today's Marks:** /6

# Day Two Try these.

CLUES

## Animals in the Zoo

**Top Tip!** Act it out.

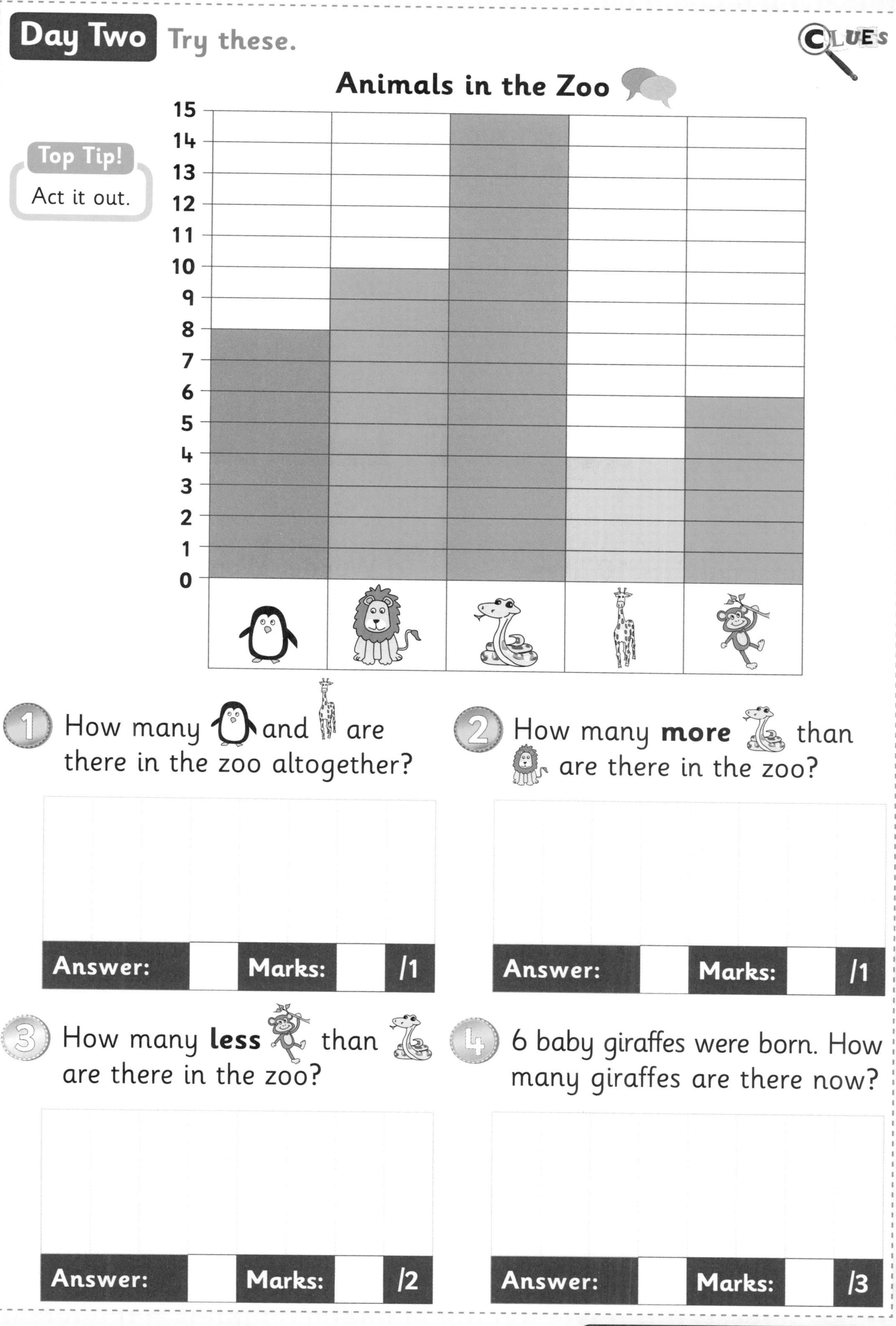


1. How many penguins and giraffes are there in the zoo altogether?

| Answer: | | Marks: | | /1 |
|---|---|---|---|---|

2. How many **more** snakes than lions are there in the zoo?

| Answer: | | Marks: | | /1 |
|---|---|---|---|---|

3. How many **less** monkeys than snakes are there in the zoo?

| Answer: | | Marks: | | /2 |
|---|---|---|---|---|

4. 6 baby giraffes were born. How many giraffes are there now?

| Answer: | | Marks: | | /3 |
|---|---|---|---|---|

Today's Marks: /7

## Day Three Try these.

Use the clues to find out how many pupils liked each superhero. Then, write the name of each superhero below the correct column in the graph.

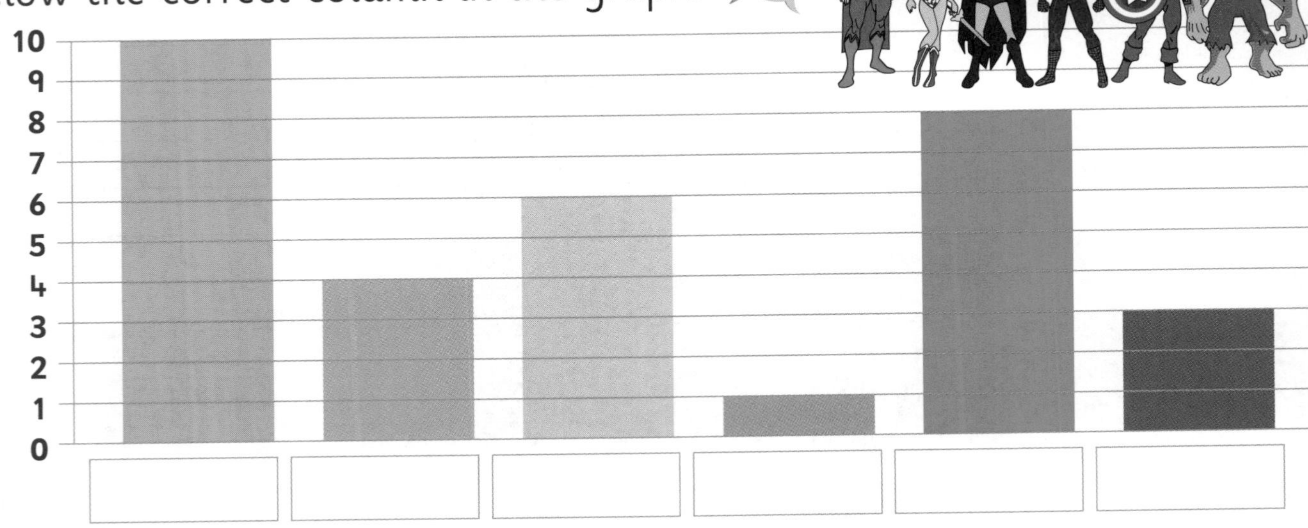


1. Superman has **10** likes. Spider-Man has **2** less likes than Superman. Only **1** pupil likes the Hulk.

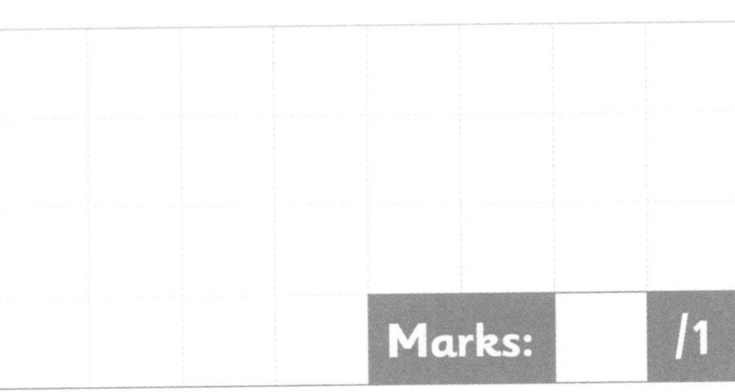


2. Wonder Woman has twice as many likes as Captain America.

Marks: /1

3. The number of Batman likes added to the number of Wonder Woman likes is equal to the number of Superman likes.

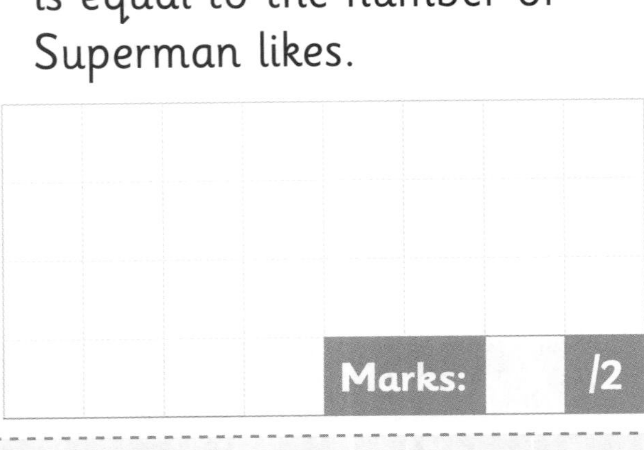


4. How many more likes does the Hulk need to be as popular as Spider-Man?

Today's Marks: /7

## Day Four Try these.

CLUES

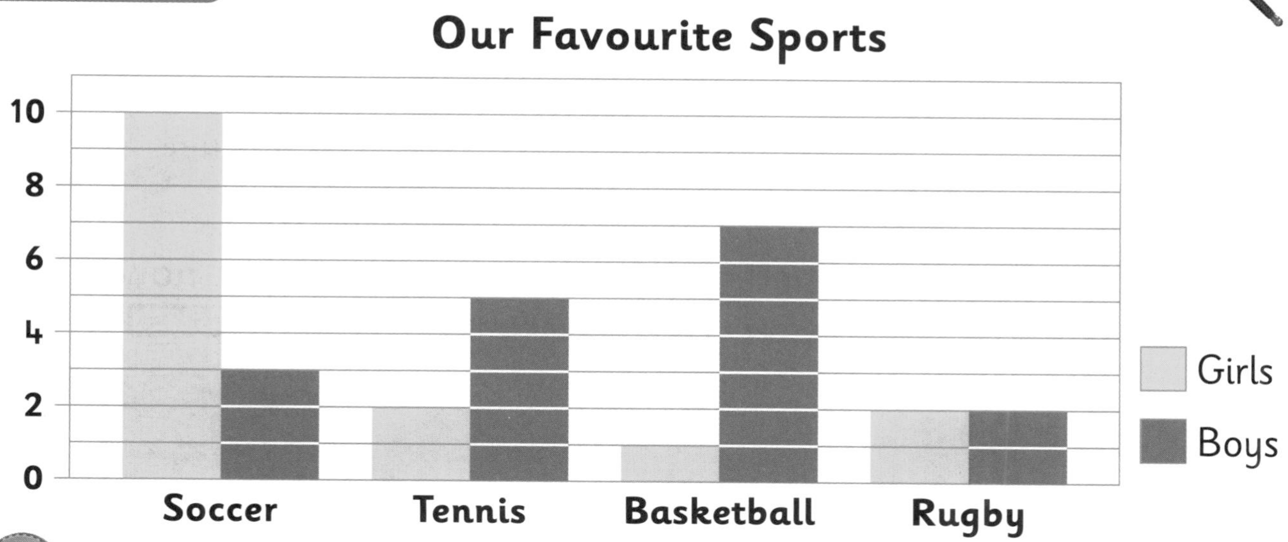

### Our Favourite Sports

| Sport | Girls | Boys |
|---|---|---|
| Soccer | 10 | 3 |
| Tennis | 2 | 5 |
| Basketball | 1 | 7 |
| Rugby | 2 | 2 |

1. Which sport is the boys' favourite and which sport is the girls' favourite?

Answers: Boys: Girls: Marks: /1

2. Which sport do the girls and the boys like equally?

Answer: Marks: /1

3. How many more girls than boys prefer soccer?

Answer: Marks: /2

4. What is the difference between the girls' and boys' votes for soccer?

Answer: Marks: /3

Today's Marks: /7

Total Marks: /27 Got this! Getting there. Need help!

I helped my friend by

## The Petting Farm

### Day One Try these.

Top Tip!
Draw a picture.

1. At the petting farm, there are **6** pigs in a pen. Count how many ears they have altogether. Estimate first.

Polly's Petting Farm

Answer: Marks: /1

2. Mammy duck and her **8** ducklings are in the pond. Count how many webbed feet are in the pond. Estimate first.

Answer: Marks: /1

3. The barrel train takes children on a trip around the farm. There are **7** barrels on the train and **2** **red** wheels on each barrel. Count how many **red** wheels there are altogether. Estimate first.

Answer: Marks: /2

4. At the petting area, there are **15** rabbits. There are **5** hutches. How many rabbits do you think sleep in each hutch?

Answer: Marks: /3



**Strand:** Number **Strand Units:** Counting and Numeration; Comparing and Ordering; Operations – addition **Strand:** Data **Strand Unit:** Representing and Interpreting Data

Today's Marks: /7

## Day Two Try these.

**Team Talk**

Reader

Calculator

Checker

Reporter

**Top Tip!**

Pair up the sheep and horses.

1. There are **15** sheep and **9** horses in a field at the petting farm. How many more sheep than horses are there?

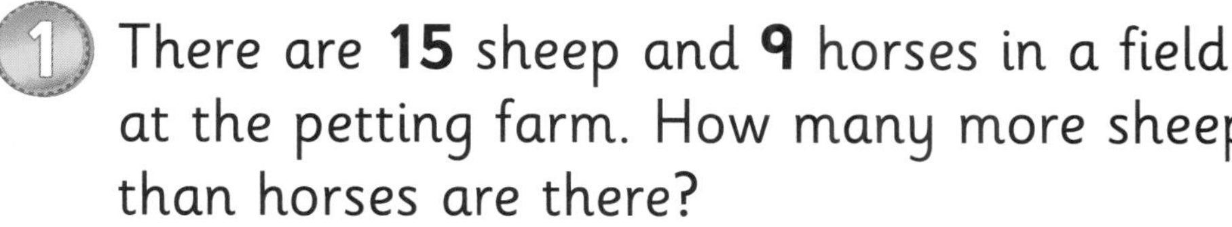

**Answer:** **Marks:** /1

2. Ace ate **19** apple slices, Jasmine ate **8** apple slices and Reid ate **11** apple slices. Put them in order, starting with the horse who ate the most.

**Answer:** **Marks:** /1

3. The farmer has painted the barrel train. She painted the **1st** barrel **red**, the **2nd** barrel **blue**, the **3rd** barrel **yellow**, the **4th** barrel **green**, the **5th** barrel **purple**, the **6th** barrel **orange** and the **7th** barrel **pink**. Colour the barrels the correct colours.

**Marks:** /2

4. There are **4** mini diggers at the petting farm. The farmer wants to buy **10** more. How many diggers will she have then?

**Answer:** **Marks:** /3

**Today's Marks:** /7

## Day Three Try these.

CLUES

1. The farmer has **6** pet mice and **6** pet guinea pigs. How many mice and guinea pigs does she have in total?

**Top Tip!**
Remember double numbers.

**Answer:** **Marks:** /1

2. The geese at the petting farm eat **5** loaves of bread in one week. How many loaves of bread do they eat in **two** weeks?

**Answer:** **Marks:** /1

3. The farmer milks the cow **twice** a day. If the farmer works for **7** days, how many times will she milk the cow?

**Answer:** **Marks:** /2

4. It costs **€4** for a child and **€8** for an adult to visit the petting farm. How much would it cost for **two** children and **one** adult to visit the petting farm?

**Joke!**
Why did the two 4s skip lunch?
Because they already 8!

**Answer:** **Marks:** /3



**Today's Marks:** /7

## Day Four Try these.

**Team Talk**

- Reader
- Calculator
- Checker
- Reporter

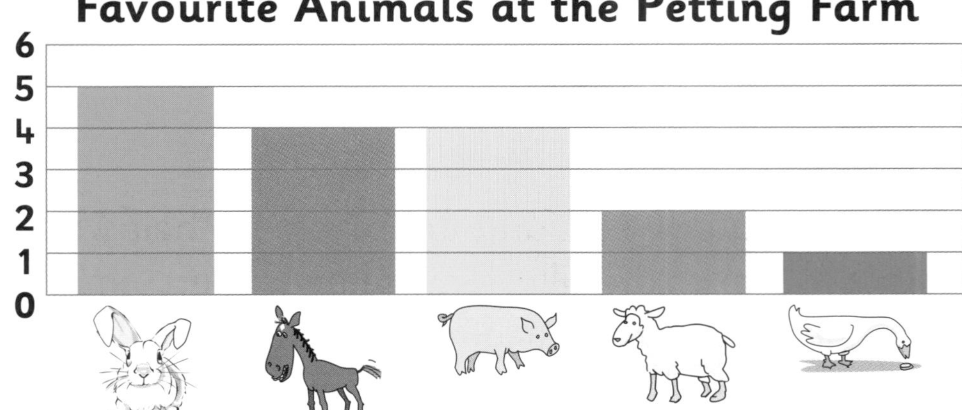


1. How many children preferred rabbits and horses altogether?

**Answer:**   **Marks:** /1

2. How many more children preferred pigs than geese?

**Answer:**   **Marks:** /2

3. What was the difference between the favourite and the least favourite animal?

**Answer:**   **Marks:** /3

**Today's Marks:** /6

## Puzzle Power

What gets wet when drying? Read the clues. Write the answer in the space below.

O before W, E after W, L after E and T before O

# 6 Strategy: Trial and Improvement

## Day One

The strategy of trial and improvement helps you to think about a number story carefully. This allows you to make a good guess and then break down your guess until you get the correct answer. Use the rough work area to keep trying and checking your work.

**Try these.**

1. Nemo the clownfish has **3** white stripes. If there are **9** white stripes in the clownfish tank at the aquarium, how many clownfish are there?

| Answer: | | Marks: | | /1 |
|---|---|---|---|---|

2. Ollie the octopus has **8** limbs. A worker at the aquarium has **8** rings. In pairs, discuss how many different ways she could put the rings on Ollie's limbs.

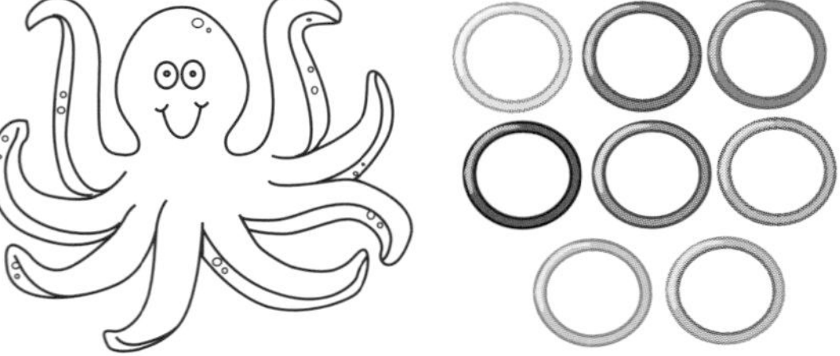

| Marks: | | /2 |
|---|---|---|

3. There are **12** starfish and **3** tanks. Draw the starfish in the tanks so that each tank has 3 more than the one before.

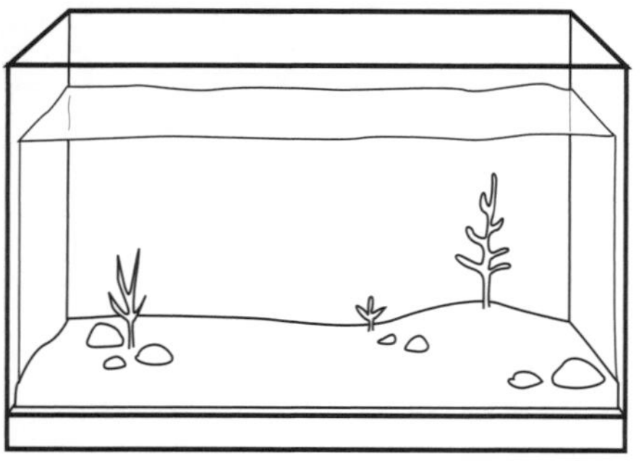

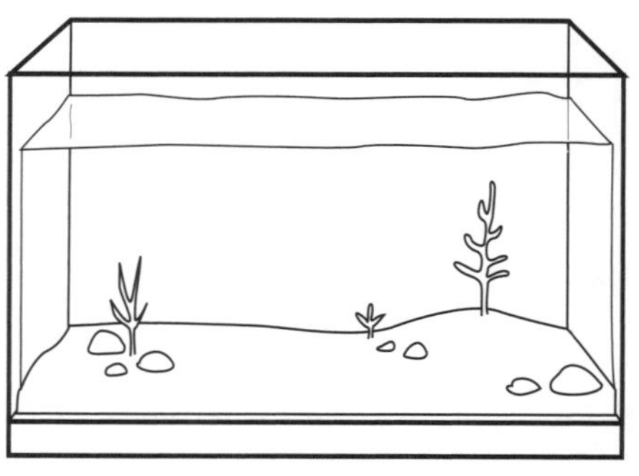

| Marks: | | /3 |
|---|---|---|



| Today's Marks: | | /6 |
|---|---|---|

## Day Two Try these.

1. Sarah and Becca were playing a game on the laptop. Each girl scored points. If they scored **4** points between them, what might their scores have been? Fill in the table.

| Sarah | Becca |
|---|---|
| 2 | |
| | |
| | |

**Top Tip!**
If the amount is too high, try less. If it is too low, try more.

Marks: /1

2. At the end of the game, Sarah had scored **twice** as many points as Becca. If their total score was **15**, how many points had each girl scored?

Answers: Sarah: Becca: Marks: /1

3. The girls played an equal number of games each day for **6** days. They played **12** games in total. How many games did they play each day?

Answer: Marks: /2

4. Out of **12** games, for every game that Becca won, Sarah won two games. How many games did each girl win?

Answers: Sarah: Becca: Marks: /3

Today's Marks: /7

## Day Three Try these.

CLUES

**1** What number goes in the middle circle on each side so that it adds up to **14**? Fill in the missing numbers.

1, 4, 2, 5, 3

Marks: /1

**2** Amelia has **2 red** blocks, **2 yellow** blocks, **2 green** blocks and **2 blue** blocks. Can you position them so no two blocks of the same colour are touching? Colour the grid to show your answer.

| | | | |
|---|---|---|---|
| | | | |
| | | | |

Marks: /1

**3** At a garage, Wayne saw motorbikes and cars. He counted **18** wheels altogther. How many motorbikes and cars might he have seen? (There is more than one correct answer.)

| Car | Motorbike |
|---|---|
| | |

Marks: /2

Rob, Leo, Tim and Sam are at the cinema.

- Rob does not want to sit next to Leo.
- Sam wants to sit between Rob and Leo.
- Tim does not want to sit next to Leo either!

In what order should the boys sit?

| Seat 1: | Seat 2: | Seat 3: | Seat 4: | Marks: /3 |
|---|---|---|---|---|



Today's Marks: /7

## Day Four Try these.

1. On Tessa's duvet cover, there are aliens with **1** eye, **2** eyes and **3** eyes. Altogether, there are **9** eyes. How many of each alien might there be? (There is more than one correct answer.)

Marks: /1

2. Every room in the tower contains a number of gold coins. Draw the route you should take to collect as many gold coins as possible. How many did you collect?

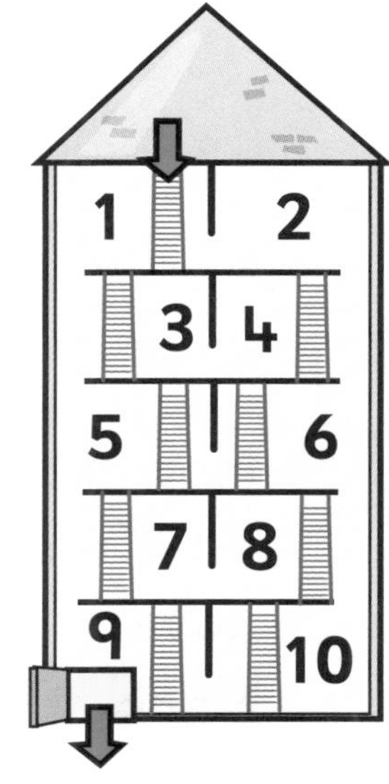


Answer: Marks: /2

3. Sharon has an equal number of brothers and sisters. Her brother Will has **twice** as many sisters as brothers. How many children are in the family?

**Top Tip!** Remember double numbers.

Answer: Marks: /3

Today's Marks: /6

Total Marks: /26

Got this!  Getting there.  Need help! 

I loved doing

Week 7

# 7  2-D Shapes

**We are learning to:** Name and describe 2-D shapes. ☐ Identify halves of 2-D shapes. ☐ Draw 2-D shapes. ☐ Identify and discuss 2-D shapes in the environment. ☐

## Day One Look at the example below.

How many corners are there altogether in a square and a triangle?

CLUES

**Circle the numbers and keywords:** corners, square, triangle

**Link with operation needed (+ or –):** Add (+).

**Use a strategy:** Draw a picture. □ △

| **Estimate and calculate:** My estimate: less than 10 | Count the corners and add them: 4 + 3 = 7 | **Answer:** 7 |
|---|---|---|

**Summarise how you got your answer:**
A square has 4 corners. A triangle has 3 corners. 4 + 3 = 7

**Try these.**

CLUES

1. How many corners do **2** rectangles have?

Answer: Marks: /1

2. How many sides are there altogether in **3** triangles?

Answer: Marks: /2

3. How many semi-circles are found in **5** circles?

Answer: Marks: /3



Today's Marks: /6

## Day Two Try these.

CLUES

Use the clues to help you draw each 2-D shape below.

1. I have **4** sides.
I have **4** corners.
My sides are all the same length.
Colour me **blue**.
What 2-D shape am I?

**Answer:** **Marks:** /1

2. I have **3** sides.
I have **3** corners.
Two of my sides are the same length.
Colour me **yellow**.
What 2-D shape am I?

**Answer:** **Marks:** /2

3. I have **2** sides.
One of my sides is curved.
One of my sides is straight.
Colour me **red**.
What 2-D shape am I?

**Answer:** **Marks:** /3

4. I have no corners.
I have **1** curved side.
Colour me **green**.
What 2-D shape am I?

**Answer:** **Marks:** /3

**Today's Marks:** /9

## Day Three Try these.

CLUES

1 How many squares in this shape have been halved? Have a go!

Answer: Marks: /1

2 What shapes have been used to cover this surface?

Answer:

Marks: /2

3 A tangram is a Chinese puzzle made of a square cut up into seven 2-D shapes. Can you name some of the shapes used to make the boat and giraffe tangrams?

Answer:

Marks: /3

### Puzzle Power

Can you work out what value each shape has? Write the values on the shapes. The first one has been done for you.

| rectangle | circle | semicircle (2) | 7 |
|---|---|---|---|
| circle | rectangle | rectangle | 9 |
| triangle | rectangle | triangle | 10 |
| 8 | 9 | 9 | |

**Top Tip!**
Use trial and improvement.



Today's Marks: /6

## Day Four Try these.

CLUES

1. Karen put her hand into the shape bag and took out **2** squares. How many corners did they have altogether?

| Answer: | | Marks: | | /1 |
|---|---|---|---|---|

2. Rory put his hand into the shape bag and took out **2** triangles. How many corners did they have altogether?

| Answer: | | Marks: | | /2 |
|---|---|---|---|---|

3. Larry cut **2** circles in half. What was he left with?

| Answer: | | Marks: | | /3 |
|---|---|---|---|---|

## Super Sleuth challenge

Today's Marks: /6

Draw a friend for Reuben the robot. You can use as many shapes as you like, but you must include:

| square | rectangle |
|---|---|
| triangle | circle |
| semi-circle | |

Total Marks: /27

Got this!  Getting there.  Need help! 

I would like to get better at

# 8 Time 1

**We are learning to:** Sequence events. ☐ Read time in hours and half-hours on a 12-hour analogue clock. ☐ Read and record time. ☐

## Day One Look at the example below.

Granny met her friends at 2 o'clock. She stayed with them for 1 hour. At what time did she go home?

**Circle the numbers and keywords:** 2 o'clock, 1 hour, what time

**Link with operation needed (+ or –):** None

**Use a strategy:**
Draw a picture.

**Estimate and calculate:**
My estimate: count on 1 hour | 2 + 1 = 3 | **Answer:** 3 o'clock

**Summarise how you got your answer:**
I counted on 1 hour later from 2 o'clock.

**Try these.**

1. On Saturday morning, Mammy went to the shop at the time shown. If she was gone for **1** hour, at what time did she return?

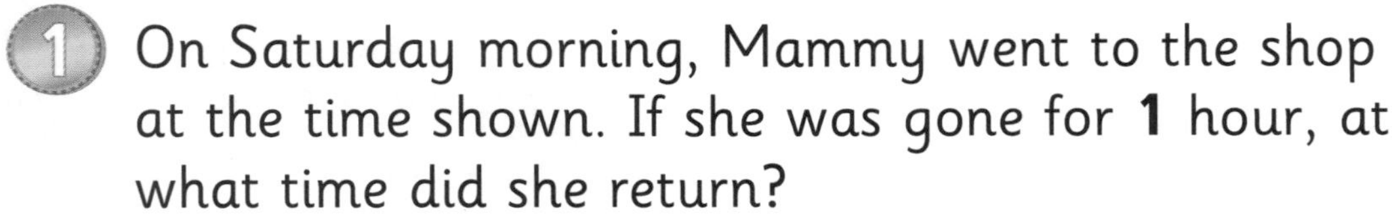

**Answer:** | **Marks:** /1

2. Gregory started his homework at the time shown. If he finished at **half past 5**, how long did he spend doing his homework?

**Answer:** | **Marks:** /2

3. Jayda walked to ballet practice. Ballet practice lasted an hour. Then, she walked home again, which took half an hour. For how long was she gone from her home?

**Answer:** | **Marks:** /3



**Today's Marks:** /6

## Day Two Try these.

1. Number the steps for making a cheese sandwich in the correct order.

| | | | | | |
|---|---|---|---|---|---|
| | Then, cut a few slices of cheese. |  | | Finally, cut the sandwich in half. |  |
| | Secondly, butter the bread. |  | 1 | Firstly, take two slices of bread. |  |
| | Next, put the second slice of bread on top. |  | | After that, put the cheese on the bread. |  |

**Marks:** /1

2. Use the word box to label the images below.

February March July October December

| | | | | |
|---|---|---|---|---|
|  |  |  |  |  |
| | | | | |



**Marks:** /2

3. Match each time of day to the correct image.

| | | | | |
|---|---|---|---|---|
|  |  |  |  |  |

| | | | | |
|---|---|---|---|---|
|  |  |  |  |  |

**Answer:** **Marks:** /3

**Today's Marks:** /6

## Day Three Try these.

### Saturday Nickelodeon TV Schedule

| | |
|---|---|
| 1. *Power Rangers* | 2. *Spongebob Squarepants* |
| 3. *Teenage Mutant Ninja Turtles* | 4. *Alvin and the Chipmunks* |
| 5. *George Lopez* | 6. *Henry Danger* |
| 7. *Cashlets* | 8. *Garfield: The Movie* |

1. For how long does *Alvin and the Chipmunks* last?

**Answer:** **Marks:** /1

2. What programme starts **1** hour after **10 o'clock**?

**Answer:** **Marks:** /2

3. If I wake up at **8 o'clock** and it takes me **half an hour** to eat breakfast, what programme will I then be ready to watch?

**Answer:**

**Marks:** /3

### Super Sleuth challenge

An egg timer lasts for 3 minutes. How many times do you think you would need to turn an egg timer before you finish tying your shoe laces?

**Today's Marks:** /6

## Day Four Try these.

1. A test takes half an hour and lunch starts at **half past 12**. What is the latest time that Miss Fortune's class can start their test in order to go for lunch on time?

Answer: Marks: /1

2. Emmet is allowed to watch **1** hour of television every night. If each episode of his favourite programme lasts for **half an hour**, how many episodes can he watch?

Answer: Marks: /2

3. Louise ran for **1** hour on Monday, for **half an hour more than that** on Wednesday and for **1 hour more than that** on Friday. For how many hours did she run in total?

Answer: Marks: /3

Today's Marks: /6

### Super Sleuth investigates

1. Can you write the numbers on the clock?
2. At what time do you think a 7-year-old child should go to bed? Draw the hands on the clock to show your answer.
3. Why do you think we need time?

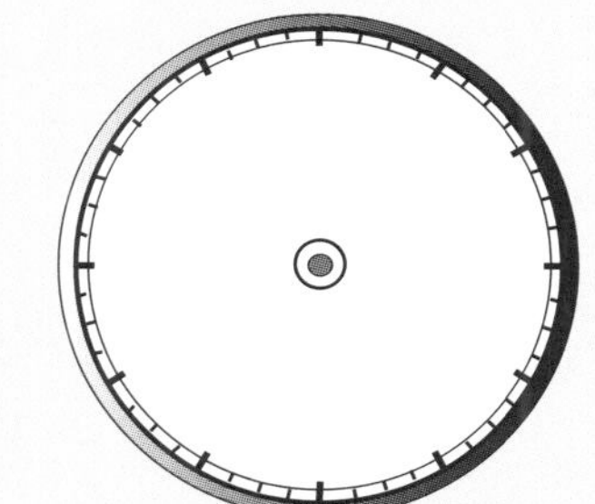

Total Marks: /24

Got this!  Getting there. 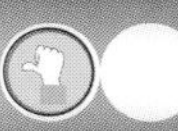 Need help! 

I enjoyed

# 9 Money

**We are learning to:** Recognise, exchange and use coins up to the value of 50 cent. ☐ Calculate how many items may be bought with a given amount. ☐

## Day One Look at the example below.

It costs 20 cent for an adult and 15 cent for a child to use the public toilets. How much is it in total for 1 adult and 1 child?

CLUES

**C**ircle the numbers and keywords:
20 cent, 15 cent, in total

**L**ink with operation needed (+ or –): Add (+).

**U**se a strategy: Act it out.

**E**stimate and calculate:

| My estimate: less than 50 cent | 20c + 15c = 35c | **Answer:** 35 cent (35c) |
|---|---|---|

**S**ummarise how you got your answer:
I added the two amounts.

**Try these.**

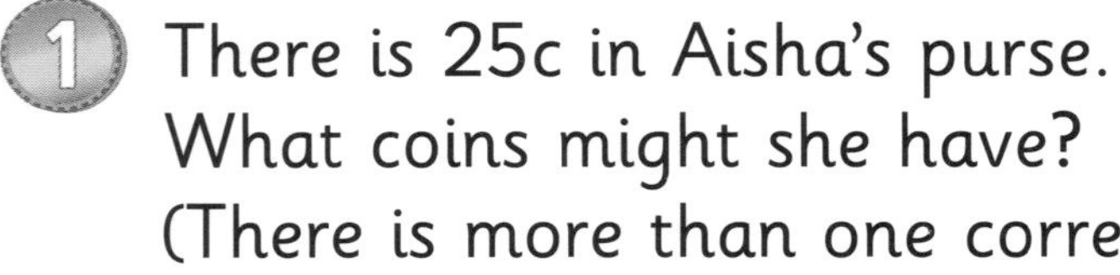

1. There is 25c in Aisha's purse. What coins might she have? (There is more than one correct answer.)

**Marks:** /1

2. What coins do I need to buy each piece of fruit?

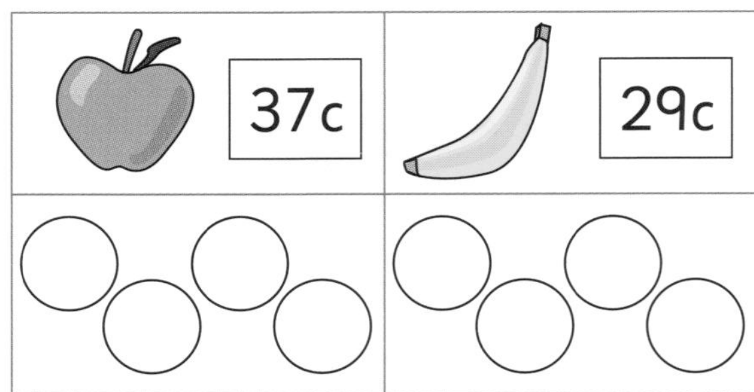


**Marks:** /2

3. If Carrie buys 2 pears, what coins will she need?

**Marks:** /3



**Today's Marks:** /6

## Day Two Try these.

CLUES

**Team Talk**

Reader

Calculator

Checker

Reporter

1. A stamp costs **48c**. Do you have enough money? Explain.

**Answer:** **Marks:** /1

2. A pencil costs **35c**. Do you have enough money? Explain.

**Answer:** **Marks:** /1

3. An eraser costs **21c**. You want to buy **2** of them. Do you have enough money? Explain.

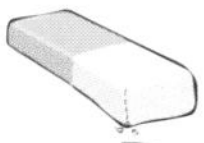

**Answer:** **Marks:** /2

4. A paperclip costs **5c**. The teacher needs to buy **5** of them. What change will she get?

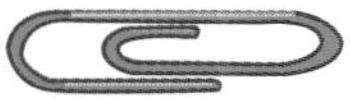

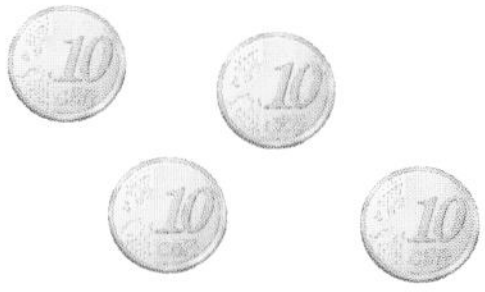

**Answer:** **Marks:** /3

**Today's Marks:** /7

## Day Three Try these.

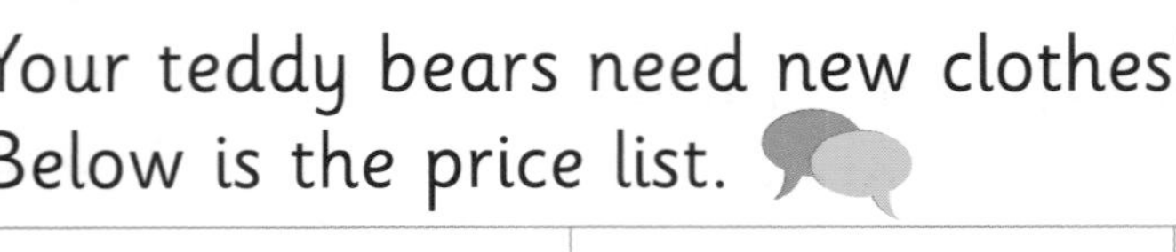

Your teddy bears need new clothes!
Below is the price list.

| | | | |
|---|---|---|---|
| 45c shoes | 14c socks | 30c shirt | 25c skirt |
| 20c shorts | 32c trousers | 48c jumper | 27c cap |

1. You have a **50c** coin. How much change will you get if you buy the shoes?

**Top Tip!** Count up to the nearest 10 to find your change.

Answer: Marks: /1

2. You have **two 20c** coins. How much will you have left if you buy the shorts?

Answer: Marks: /1

3. You have a **20c** coin and a **10c** coin. How much will you have left if you buy the cap?

Answer: Marks: /2

4. You have a **50c** coin. What **two** items cost exactly this amount?

**Top Tip!** Use trial and improvement.

Answer: Marks: /3



Today's Marks: /7

## Day Four Try these.

**Team Talk**

Reader
Calculator
Checker
Reporter

1. Which is better value:
   (a) **2** comics for **34c** or
   (b) **1** comic for **19c**?

**Answer:** ______ **Marks:** /1

2. Which is better value: (a) **10** Pokémon cards for **40c** or (b) **1** Pokémon card for **3c**?

**Answer:** ______ **Marks:** /2

3. Which is better value:
   (a) **10** stickers for **50c** or
   (b) **1** sticker for **6c**?

**Answer:** ______ **Marks:** /3

**Today's Marks:** /6

## Super Sleuth challenge

Make 50c by adding the coins across or downwards. Shade the correct answers.

| | | | | |
|---|---|---|---|---|
| 10 | 10 | 10 | 10 | 10 |
| 10 | 20 | 5 | 20 | 5 |
| 10 | 5 | 10 | 10 | 5 |
| 20 | 5 | 5 | 10 | 10 |

**Total Marks:** /26 **Got this!**  **Getting there.**  **Need help!** 

**My favourite activity was** ______

# 10 Place Value 1

**We are learning to:** Explore, identify and record place value 0–99. ☐

## Day One Look at the example below.

I have fewer than 20 stickers in my album. I have 1 full ten number frame and 5 left over. How many stickers do I have?

**Circle the numbers and keywords:**
1 ten number frame, 5 left over

**Link with operation needed (+ or –):** Add (+).

**Use a strategy:** Draw a picture.

**Estimate and calculate:**
My estimate: I know that there are 10 units in 1 ten.

| | T | U |
|---|---|---|
| | 1 | 0 |
| + | | 5 |
| | 1 | 5 |

**Answer:** 15

**Summarise how you got your answer:**
I added 1 ten and 5 units.

**Try these.**

1. Colour the number frames to show the number of sweets above.

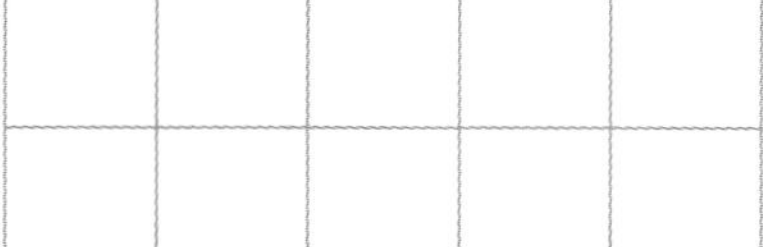 

Marks: /1

2. How many more sweets would it take to fill both number frames above? Colour this number frame to show the answer.

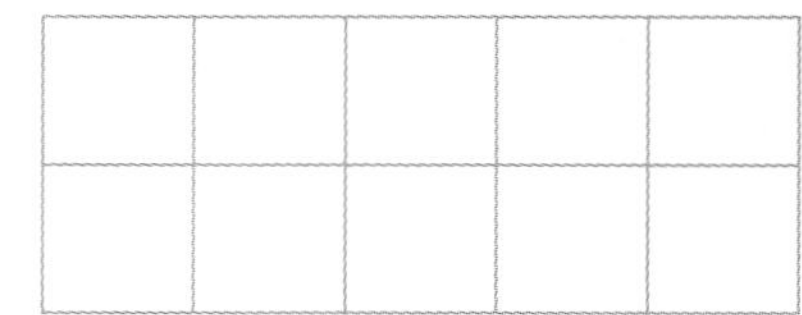

Marks: /2

3. If three sweets were eaten, how many were left? Colour this number frame to show the answer.

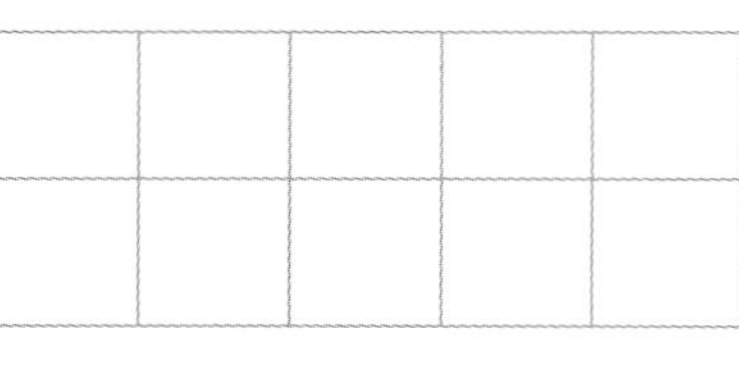

Marks: /3



Today's Marks: /6

## Day Two Try these.

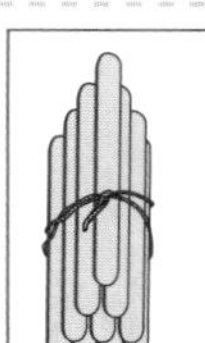
= 1 ten

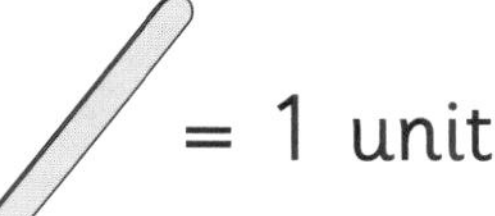
= 1 unit

1. Amy made a star using lollipop sticks. How many tens and units did she use?

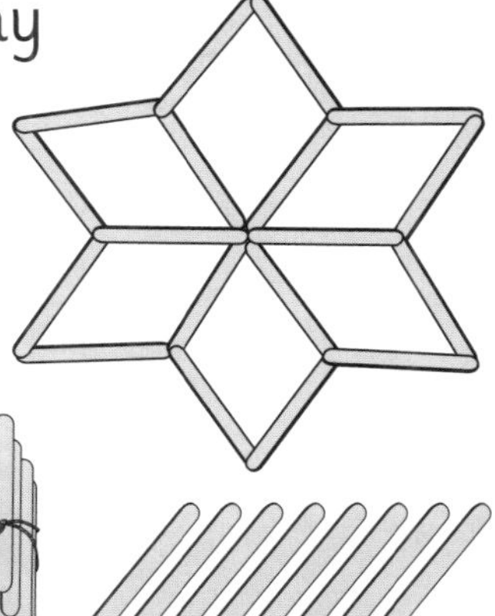

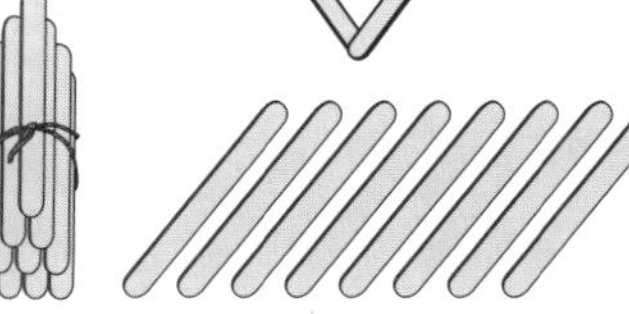

Answer: Marks: /1

2. Andrew added **2** more units to the lollipop sticks below to make a basket. How many tens and units did he use altogther?

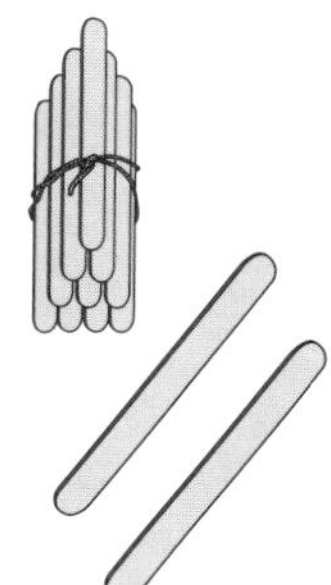

Answer: Marks: /1

3. Mark wants to make a chair using **19** lollipop sticks. How many more tens and units does he need?

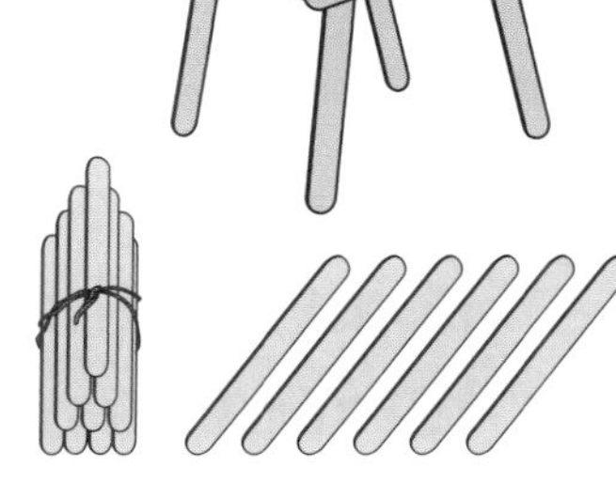

Answer: Marks: /2

4. Mira and Kelly both want to make a table using **10** lollipop sticks **each**. How many tens and units do they need?

Answer: Marks: /3

Today's Marks: /7

## Day Three Try these.

1. Jessica scored **5** points in the first half of a camogie match and **6** points in the second half. Colour the tens and units to show her total points.

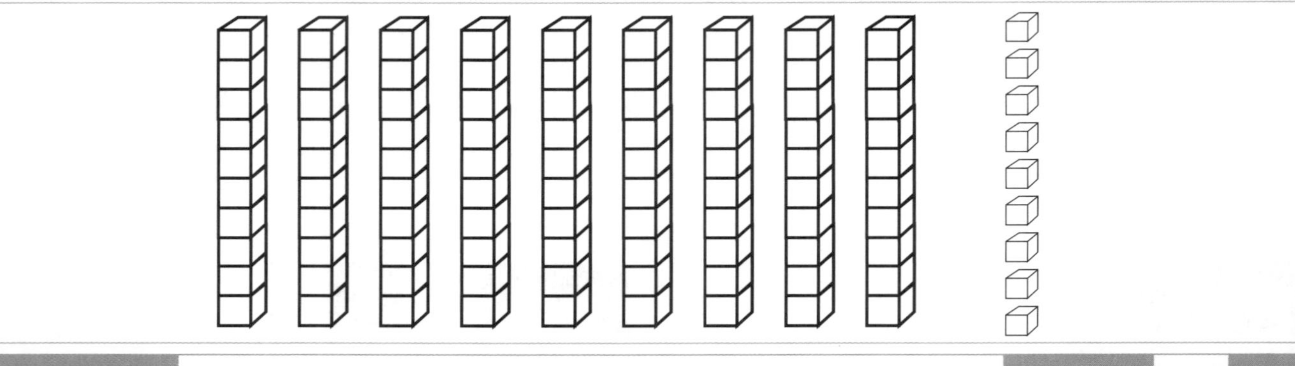

| Answer: | tens and | units = | Marks: | /1 |
|---|---|---|---|---|

2. Munster scored **6** tries in their first rugby match, **6** tries in their second match and **3** tries in their third match. Colour the tens and units to show their total tries.

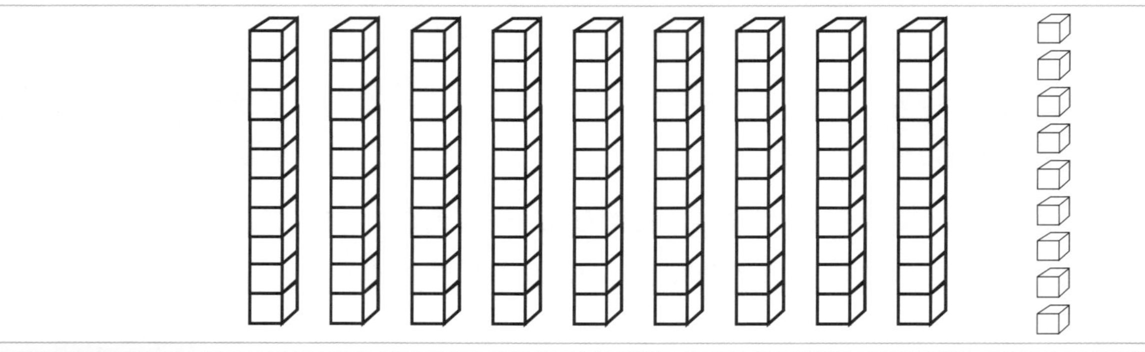

| Answer: | tens and | units = | Marks: | /2 |
|---|---|---|---|---|

3. Clare scored **9** points in the first half of a football match and **8** points in the second half. Colour the tens and units to show her total points.

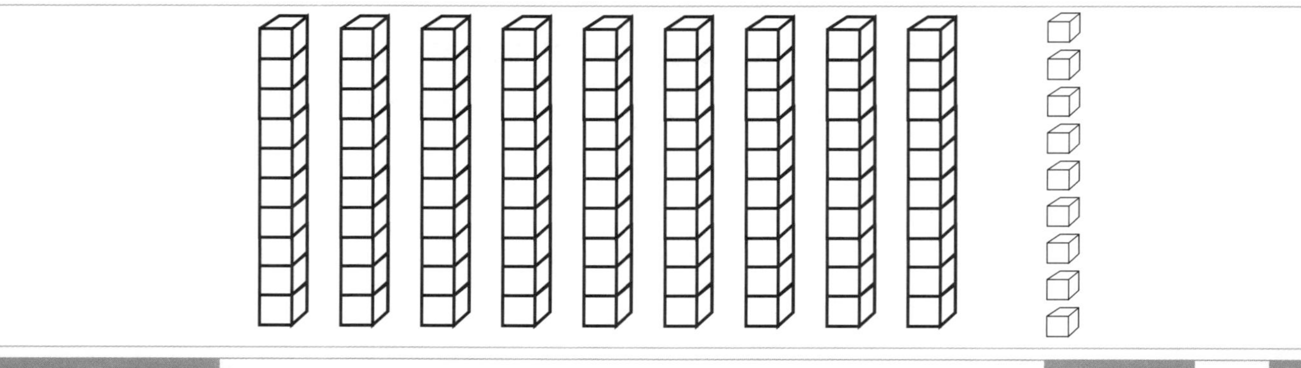

| Answer: | tens and | units = | Marks: | /3 |
|---|---|---|---|---|

Today's Marks: /6

## Day Four Try these.

| 10 | 1 |
|---|---|
| 20 | 2 |
| 30 | 3 |
| 40 | 4 |
| 50 | 5 |
| 60 | 6 |
| 70 | 7 |
| 80 | 8 |
| 90 | 9 |

1. Look at the tens and units cards. Which two cards should you use to make **25**?

   Answer: Marks: /1

2. Which two cards should you use to make the **answer** to 13 + 3?

   Answer: Marks: /2

3. Which two cards should you use to make the **answer** to 36 – 4?

   Answer: Marks: /3

Today's Marks: /6

## Super Sleuth challenge

Roll a pair of dice. In your copy, use the numbers that you have rolled to make a two-digit number. Then, write the tens and units. Next, draw the tens and units. Finally, write a number sentence using the tens and units. Play as many times as you like.

| Roll | Number | | Draw | Write |
|---|---|---|---|---|
| | T | U | | |
| I roll a 3 and a 7. My number will be **37**. | 3 | 7 | | 30 + 7 = 37 |

Total Marks: /25

Got this!  Getting there.  Need help! 

I helped my friend by

# 11 Revision 2

## The Toy Shop

### Day One Try these.

1. What 2-D shapes can you find in the teddy?

Answer:

Marks: /1

2. Design 2 rectangular scarves for the teddy. How many **edges** do they have altogether?

Answer: Marks: /1

3. Look at the teddy's nose. How many **corners** would there be in **3** of these shapes?

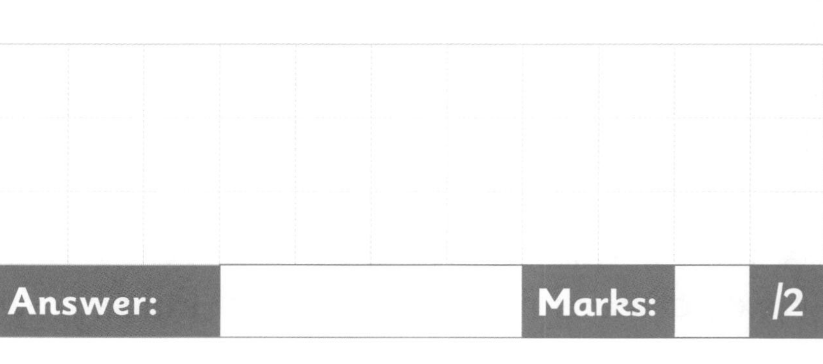

Answer: Marks: /2

4. Design a stuffed animal or another toy using at least **5** different 2-D shapes. (You can use them as many times as you like.)

Marks: /3



**Strand:** Shape and Space **Strand Unit:** 2-D Shapes
**Strand:** Measures **Strand Units:** Time; Money **Strand:** Number **Strand Unit:** Place Value

Today's Marks: /7

## Day Two Try these.

1. Three children are queuing outside a toy shop. Victor is the last in the queue. Ross is before Victor and Jenny is before Ross. Who is **second** in the queue?

**Answer:** **Marks:** /1

2. At the toy shop, the owner reads a story for the local children after school. At what time do you think this event should take place?

**Answer:** **Marks:** /1

3. A puppet show takes place four times during the day at the toy shop. Number the times in the correct order.

| Puppet Show Times | |
|---|---|
| | 3 o'clock |
| | half past 1 |
| | 5 o'clock |
| | half past 11 |

**Marks:** /2

4. The toy shop opens at 10 o'clock in the morning. Every hour, the workers take a break. At what time is their second break?

**Answer:** **Marks:** /3

## Day Three Try these.

1. A teddy's jumper costs **55c**. Draw the coins you would need to buy a jumper.

Marks: /1

2. If you have two **20c** coins, do you have enough money to buy a teddy's shirt for **38c**? Explain.

Answer:

Marks: /1

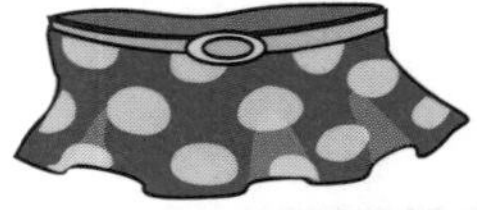

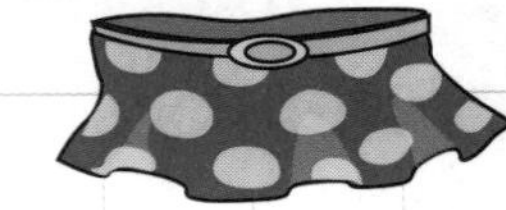

3. You have a **20c** coin. How much more money do you need to buy two skirts for **12c** each?

Answer:

Marks: /2

4. You have a **50c** coin. How much change will you get if you buy a pair of socks for **15c** and a pair of shoes for **32c**?

Answer:

Marks: /3



Today's Marks: /7

## Day Four Try these.

CLUES

1. The toy shop sold **14** teddies on Monday. Colour the number frames to show the number sold.

| | | | | |
|---|---|---|---|---|
| | | | | |
| | | | | |

| | | | | |
|---|---|---|---|---|
| | | | | |
| | | | | |

Marks: /1

2. Double the number of teddies was sold on Tuesday than on Monday. How many were sold on Tuesday?

Marks: /2

3. The toy shop got a delivery of **16 units** of jackets and **22 units** of dresses on Wednesday. How many items were delivered? Record your answer in tens and units.

Answer:

Marks: /3

Today's Marks: /6

## Puzzle Power

Using three different colours, shade the numbers needed to make 26, 34 and 71.

| 10 | 20 | 30 | 40 | 50 | 60 | 70 | 80 |
|---|---|---|---|---|---|---|---|
| 1 | 2 | 3 | 4 | 5 | 6 | 7 | 8 |

# 12 Strategy: Act It Out

## Day One

The act-it-out strategy helps you to break down a number story by using concrete materials. This might involve using blocks, teddy bears, unifix cubes, counters, lollipop sticks or money to act out the story. This strategy can be fun if you like to be active while you work!

Try these.

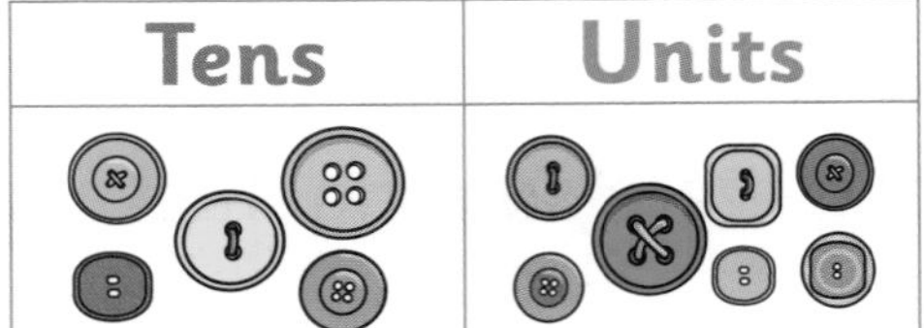


**Top Tip!** Count the buttons.

1. Mr Smith showed his class how to make a two-digit number using 12 buttons. Look at the image. What two-digit number did he give as an example?

   Answer: Marks: /1

2. If you take **1** button from the units and place it with the tens, what number will you make?

   Answer: Marks: /1

3. How many buttons would you need to make the number **46**?

   Answer: Marks: /2

4. If you have **8** buttons, what number can you make? (There is more than one answer.)

   Answer: Marks: /3

Today's Marks: /7

## Day Two Try these.

**Top Tip!** Use cubes to help you.

CLUES

1. Mammy has **4** items on her shopping list. She wants to buy **3** of each item on the list. How many items will she buy in total?

Shopping list:
- Apples
- Bananas
- Scones
- Carrots

**Answer:** | **Marks:** /1

2. **37** people are going on a mini-bus tour. A mini-bus holds only **10** passengers. How many mini-buses will be needed for the whole group?

**Answer:** | **Marks:** /1

3. Darcy can make **2** origami birds in an hour. How many can she make in **5** hours?

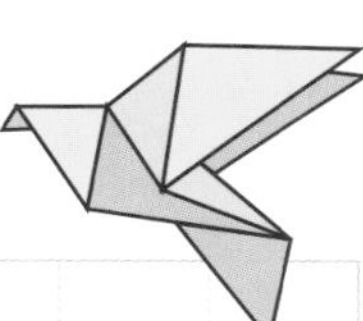

**Answer:** | **Marks:** /2

4. Find a way to swap the red frogs and the green frogs. How many moves does it take?

The rules are:
- You can only move one place forwards or backwards at a time.
- Only one frog can sit on each lily pad at a time.
- The frogs can jump over one another.

**Answer:** | **Marks:** /3

**Today's Marks:** /7

## Day Three Try these.

**Top Tip!** Use counters to help you.

CLUES

1. As the Pied Piper left the town of Hamelin, there were **32** legs in total following him! There was an equal number of human legs and rat legs. How many humans and rats were there? Remember how many legs they each have!

**Answer:** **Marks:** /1

2. There are **3** tennis balls in a tube and **4** golf balls in a box. Daddy bought **30** balls in total. How many tubes and boxes could he have bought?

**Answer:** **Marks:** /1

3. Heather had **17** dolls. She arranged them into **4** toy boxes. How might she have arranged them?

**Answer:** **Marks:** /2

4. There were **4** people at a dinner party. They all shook hands on arrival. How many handshakes were exchanged?

**Top Tip!** Act it out.

**Answer:** **Marks:** /3



**Today's Marks:** /7

## Day Four Try these.

1. Cruz blew up a number of balloons for a party. He had **3 red** balloons. He had **6 more blue** balloons than red balloons and **1 less green** balloon than blue balloons. How many balloons did he have altogether?

**Answer:** **Marks:** /1

2. Four children are standing in a line. Kevin is taller than Jessica, but not as tall as Evan. David is taller than Evan. Write their names in order from the shortest to the tallest child.

**Answer:** **Marks:** /2

3. Can you remove one matchstick to make this statement true?

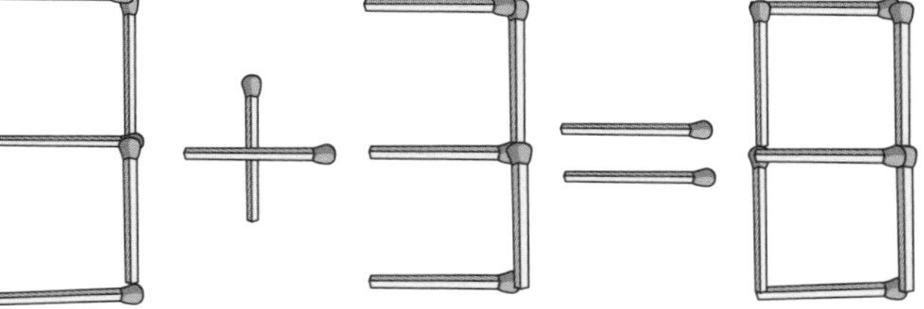

**Joke!**

Why is 6 afraid of 7?

Because 7 8 9!

**Answer:** **Marks:** /3

**Today's Marks:** /6

**Total Marks:** /27

**Got this!**  **Getting there.**  **Need help!** 

**I loved doing**

# 13 Length

**We are learning to:** Investigate length using non-standard units. ☐
Investigate length using standard units (metres). ☐

**Day One** Look at the example below.

How many rulers are needed to form a line across the whiteboard?

CLUES

**C**ircle the numbers and keywords: ruler, whiteboard

**L**ink with operation needed (+ or –): None

**U**se a strategy: Pattern

**E**stimate and calculate:

| My estimate: fewer than 15 | Try it out with a group of your classmates! | **Answer:** about 10 |
|---|---|---|

**S**ummarise how you got your answer:
I counted how many rulers were needed.

**Try these.**

CLUES

1. Number the objects in order from shortest to longest.

| | | | | |
|---|---|---|---|---|
| | | | | |
| cube | straw | pencil | eraser | paper clip |

**Marks:** /1

2. How many straws are needed to measure the length of your arm from shoulder to fingertips?

**Top Tip!** Act it out.

**Answer:** **Marks:** /2

3. The length of your foot takes up how many erasers? Compare your foot with a classmate's foot. Whose foot is longer?

**Answer:** **Marks:** /3

**Today's Marks:** /6

## Day Two Try these.

1. Choose three crayons and arrange them in order from shortest to longest. Measure them using cubes.

Marks: /1

2. Look around your classroom and find items that you can measure. Arrange them in order from longest to shortest. Measure them using paper clips.

Marks: /1

3. If it takes **6** lollipop sticks to measure a table, how many lollipop sticks would it take to measure **2** tables?

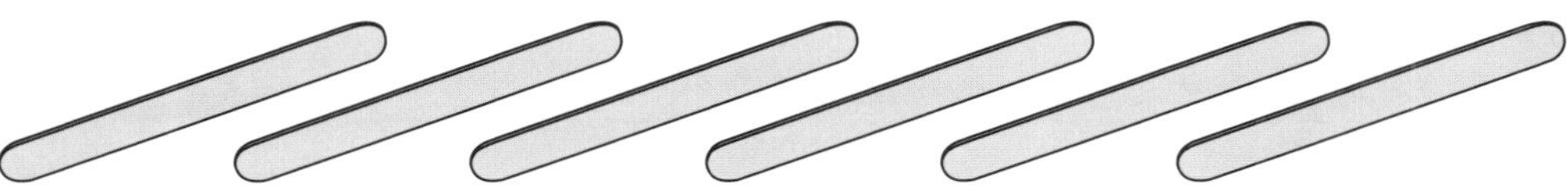

Answer: Marks: /2

4. If **4** pencil cases are **8** straws long and **2** school bags are **10** straws long, how many straws longer than a pencil case is a school bag?

Answer: Marks: /3

Today's Marks: /7

## Day Three Try these.

CLUES

**Team Talk**

Reader
Calculator
Checker
Reporter

1. The red boat is **5** metres long. The blue boat is **1** metre shorter than the red boat. What is the length of the blue boat?

**Answer:** | **Marks:** /1

2. The large school bus is **10** metres long. The small school bus is **4** metres shorter. What is the length of the small school bus?

**Answer:** | **Marks:** /1

3. A parish hall was **20** metres in length, but an extra room was built, measuring **4** metres in length. What is the length of the parish hall now?

**Answer:** | **Marks:** /2

4. If the total length of two ladders is **10** metres and one of them measures **7** metres, what is the length of the other ladder?

**Answer:** | **Marks:** /3



**Today's Marks:** /7

## Day Four Try these.

 If a knight's sword was **1** metre in length, what was the length of **3** swords?

**Answer:** Marks: /1

 A basketball court is **15** metres in length. What is the total length of **2** basketball courts?

**Answer:** Marks: /2

**Joke!**

Why did the boy keep a ruler under his bed?

To see how long he would sleep!

3. The length of a playground was increased from **43** metres to **54** metres. What was the increase in length?

**Answer:** Marks: /3

**Today's Marks:** /6

## Super Sleuth investigates

1. How many of Baby Bear's bed would it take to measure the length of Daddy Bear's bed?
2. Do you think Daddy Bear's bed is longer or shorter than 1 metre?

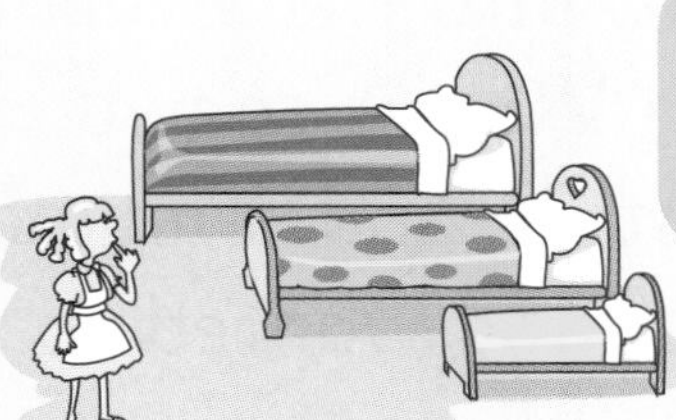

**Top Tip!**

You are over 1 metre tall.

**Total Marks:** /26

**Got this!**  **Getting there.**  **Need help!** 

I would like to get better at

# 14  Subtraction

**We are learning to:** Subtract numbers within 99. ☐ Recall mental strategies for subtraction facts 0–20. ☐ Make number sentences and stories. ☐

## Day One Look at the example below.

Daddy had 8 screwdrivers, but he lost 2.
How many does he have left?

CLUES

**C**ircle the numbers and keywords: 8, lost 2, left

**L**ink with operation needed (+ or –): Subtract (–).

**U**se a strategy: Draw a picture.

**E**stimate and calculate:

| My estimate: a single-digit answer | $8 - 2 = 6$ | **Answer:** 6 |
|---|---|---|

**S**ummarise how you got your answer:
He lost 2 screwdrivers, so I took away 2 from 8.

**Try these.**

CLUES

1. There were **9** rabbits in a pet shop. **3** were sold. How many are still in the pet shop?

| Answer: | | Marks: | | /1 |
|---|---|---|---|---|

2. Carly has **12** books from the *Diary of a Wimpy Kid* series. Ross only has **7**. How many less does he have?

| Answer: | | Marks: | | /2 |
|---|---|---|---|---|

3. Jordi went into the sweet shop with **20c**. A chewy sweet cost **2c** and a lollipop cost **10c**. If he wanted to spend all of his money, what could he buy?

| Answer: | | Marks: | | /3 |
|---|---|---|---|---|



Today's Marks: ☐ /6

## Day Two Try these.

1 Max is **20** years old. His sister is **5** years younger. What age is his sister?

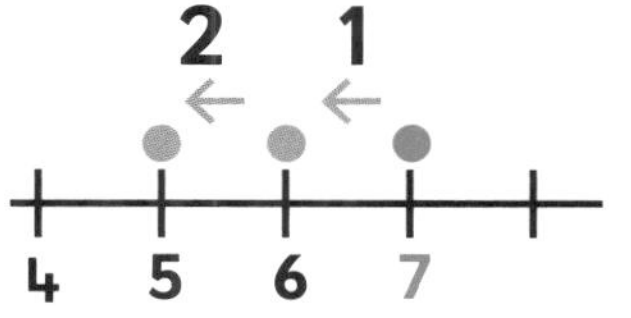

**Top Tip!**
When we subtract, we count backwards. We can use a number line to help.

**Answer:** **Marks:** /1

2 Mikey got **10** spellings right in his test. His friend Luke got **3 less** than him right. How many spellings did Luke get right?

**Answer:** **Marks:** /1

3 Mr Timmons has **12** toffees. Mr Bohane has **6** toffees. How many **fewer** does Mr Bohane have?

**Top Tip!**
Act it out.

**Answer:** **Marks:** /2

4 Granny needs **16** apples to make **two** apple tarts. How many apples would she need to make **one** apple tart?

**Answer:** **Marks:** /3

**Today's Marks:** /7

## Day Three Try these.

1. A number of cars drove out of a car park and there were **15** cars left. Make up your own number sentence for this number story.

| Answer: | – = 15 | Marks: | | /1 |
|---|---|---|---|---|

**Rhyme**

Subtract, subtract, just take away.
Fewer or less is what they say.
Decrease or minus, they all mean the same.
The difference matters in every game.

2. Sabina opened a box of chocolates and gave **2** to her friend. How many chocolates do you think were in the box to begin with? Make up your own number sentence for this number story.

| Answer: | – = | Marks: | | /1 |
|---|---|---|---|---|

3. Mammy baked **20** cookies and gave a number of them to Mrs Kelly next door. Make up your own number sentence for this number story.

| Answer: | – = | Marks: | | /2 |
|---|---|---|---|---|

4. Josephine received **12** birthday presents in total. She received **2** from her grandparents and **2** from her parents. The rest were from her friends. How many presents did she receive from her friends?

| Answer: | – = | Marks: | | /3 |
|---|---|---|---|---|

Today's Marks: /7

## Day Four Try these.

1. **16** children were on the roundabout. **9** children got off to go on the slide. How many children remained on the roundabout?

Answer: Marks: /1

2. There are **15** bars on a climbing frame. Sandy has climbed **4** of them. How many does she have left to climb?

Answer: Marks: /2

3. **11** children would like to have a go on a see-saw. If there are **4** see-saws in the playground, how many children will have to wait their turn?

Answer: Marks: /3

Today's Marks: /6

## Super Sleuth challenge

A clever spy has hidden number sentences involving subtraction in the grid. How many can you find? Follow the numbers downwards or across and colour in the number sentences.

| | | | | | | | | | |
|---|---|---|---|---|---|---|---|---|---|
| 2 | 5 | 3 | 2 | 4 | 1 | 6 | 9 | | |
| | 0 | 7 | 1 | 8 | 3 | 2 | 0 | 7 | |
| | | 6 | 3 | 3 | 2 | 4 | 9 | 2 | 7 |
| 8 | 1 | 1 | 9 | 2 | 1 | 6 | 3 | | |
| | 9 | 4 | 5 | 7 | 0 | 8 | 3 | 2 | |
| | | 6 | 4 | 2 | 1 | 5 | 9 | 6 | 3 |
| 7 | 2 | 5 | 1 | 0 | 9 | 3 | 6 | | |
| | 7 | 4 | 3 | 1 | 5 | 8 | 4 | 4 | |

Total Marks: /26

Got this!  Getting there.  Need help! 

I enjoyed

# 15 Spatial Awareness

**We are learning to:** Explore and use the language of spatial relations. ☐ Use direction words. ☐ Follow simple directions. ☐

## Day One Look at the example below.

Build a tower using 1 green, 1 yellow and 1 blue block. Put the green block at the top with the blue block below it. Where is the yellow block? Draw your tower.

CLUES

**Circle the numbers and keywords:**
green block, yellow block, blue block

**Link with operation needed (+ or –):** None

**Use a strategy:** Act it out with real blocks and draw a picture.

**Estimate and calculate:**

| My estimate: The blocks will be stacked. | Stack the blocks in the correct order. | **Answer:** The yellow block is at the bottom. |
|---|---|---|

**Summarise how you got your answer:**
I drew a diagram of the tower.

**Try these.**

CLUES

1. Draw a rainbow. Draw a flower **below** the rainbow and a cloud **above** the rainbow.

Marks: /1

2. Write your name in the top right corner of the box. Draw two circles in the bottom left corner. Draw a hat above the circles.

Marks: /2

3. Colour the stars in the correct order. The **red** star is between the **green** and **blue** stars. The **yellow** star is first in the row and the **green** star comes after the **yellow** star.

☆ ☆ ☆ ☆

Marks: /3



Today's Marks: /6

## Day Two Try these.

**Top Tip!** The hand that forms an 'L' is your left hand and left side.

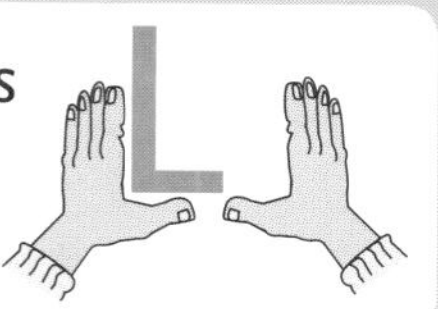

1. Draw a ⬤ on the left hand and a ▬ on the right hand.

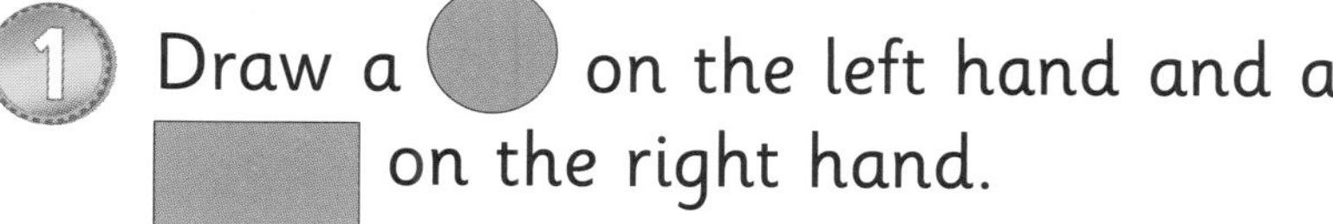

**Marks:** /1

2. Start at the star. Go 5 colours around the wheel to the right. What colour do you land on?

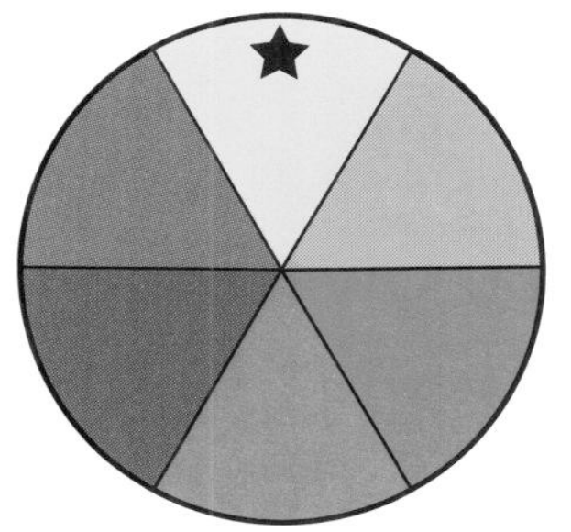

**Answer:** **Marks:** /2

3. Start at the window with a star. Go left 2 windows and then right 4 windows. What symbol do you land on?

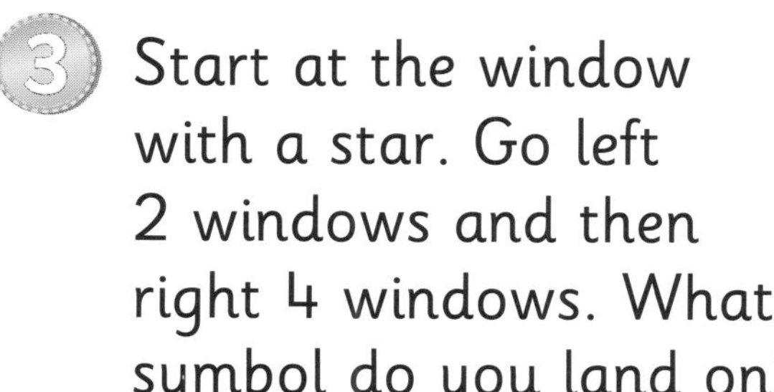

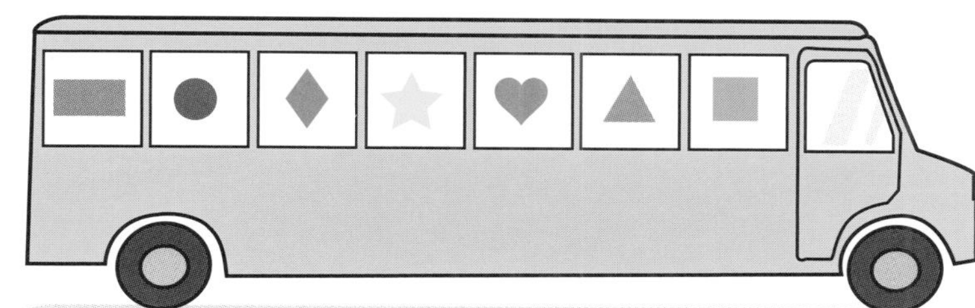

**Answer:** **Marks:** /3

## Super Sleuth investigates

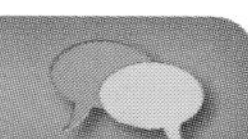

In pairs, use the grid to test your partner with the following questions:

- What shape is to the left of the brown circle?
- What shape is to the right of the pink rectangle?
- What shape is to the left of the green star?
- What shape is to the right of the pink triangle?

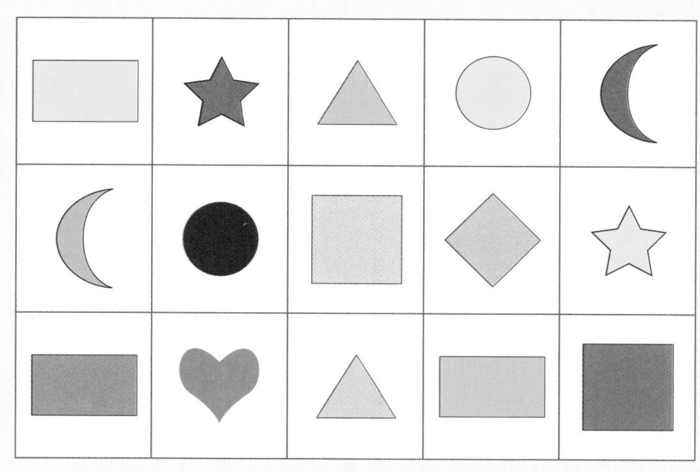

Make up some questions of your own.

**Today's Marks:** /6

## Day Three Try these.

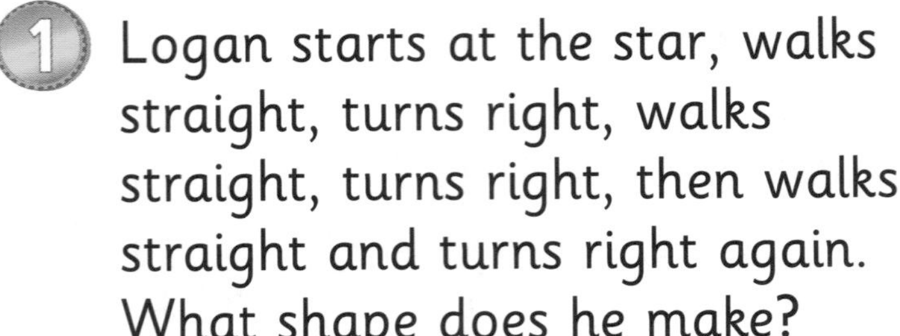

1. Logan starts at the star, walks straight, turns right, walks straight, turns right, then walks straight and turns right again. What shape does he make?

**Answer:** **Marks:** /1

2. This racetrack is shaped like the letter 'V'. Give Edmund directions to get from the start to the finish and back again.

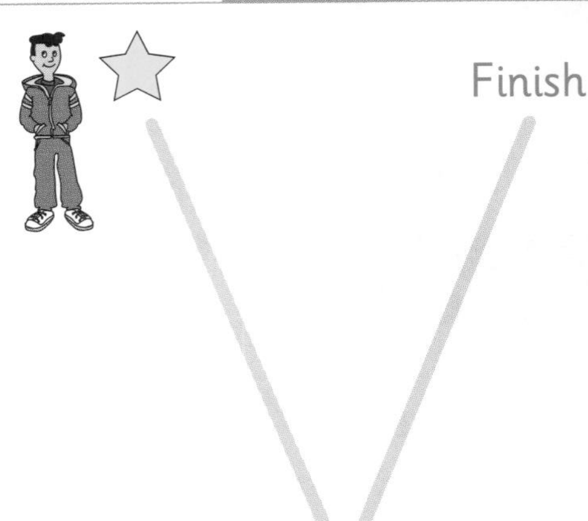


**Answer:**

**Marks:** /1

3. What shapes can you and your friends make with your bodies? Try them out!

**Answer:**

**Marks:** /2

4. You can also make letter shapes with your body. Can you name the letters that are easy to make?

**Answer:** **Marks:** /3

**Today's Marks:** /7

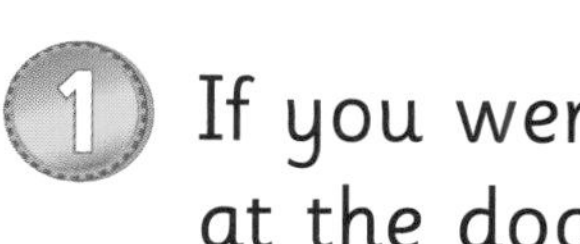


Try these.

CLUES

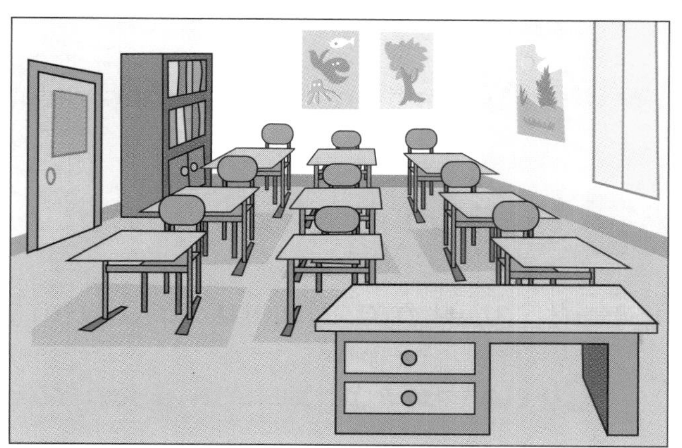

1 If you were standing at the door, what way would you turn to get to the bookcase?

| Answer: | | Marks: | /1 |
|---|---|---|---|

2 How would you get from the teacher's table to the door?

| Answer: | | Marks: | /2 |
|---|---|---|---|

3 If you were standing at the window, how would you get to the 3rd desk in the front row?

| Answer: | | Marks: | /3 |
|---|---|---|---|

Today's Marks: /6

## Puzzle power

Where would the 'X' end up if it moved 2 squares to the right, 2 squares down, 1 square to the left and 1 square up?

## Puzzle power

What goes down, but never goes up?

- Between 'R' and 'I' is 'A'.
- 'R' goes on the left.
- 'N' goes on the right.

Total Marks: /25

Got this!  Getting there.  Need help! 

My favourite activity was

# 16 Place Value 2

**We are learning to:** Explore, identify and record place value 0–99. ☐

## Day One Look at the example below.

If I have €34, how many tens and units do I have?

**Circle the numbers and keywords:** €34, tens, units

**Link with operation needed (+ or –):** None

**Use a strategy:** Draw a diagram.

**Estimate and calculate:**

My estimate: I know that there are 10 units in 1 ten.

| T | U |
|---|---|
| 3 | 4 |

**Answer:** 3 tens and 4 units

**Summarise how you got your answer:**

I know that every digit has a value and I know my tens and units.

**Try these.**

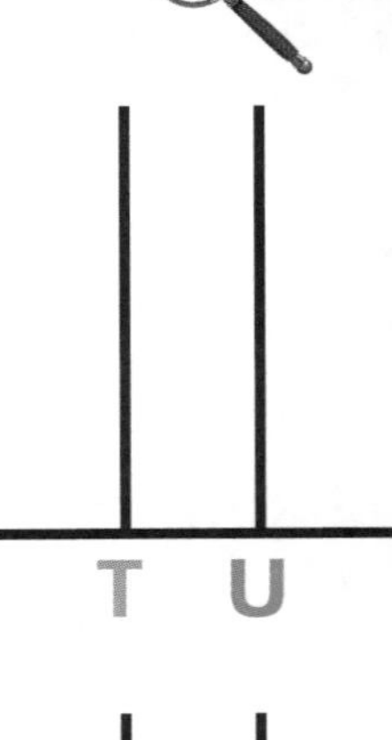


1. If there are **5** beads on the tens line and **3** beads on the units line, what number is created?

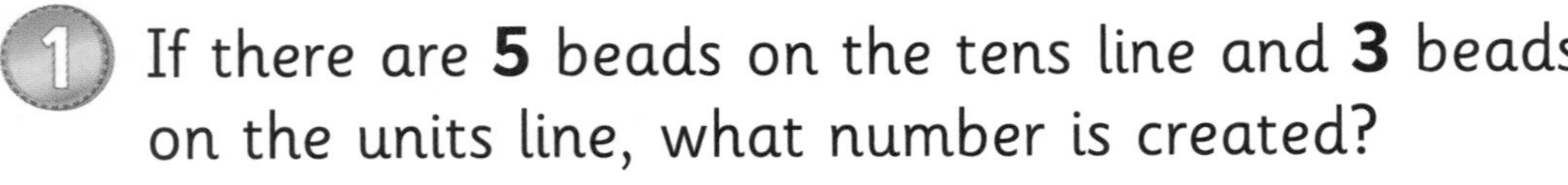

**Answer:** **Marks:** /1

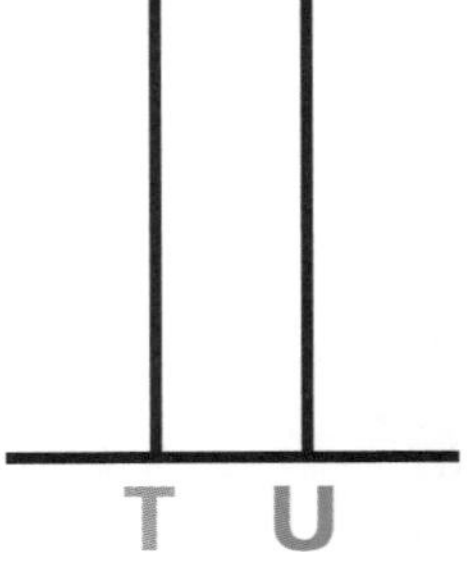


2. If you had **2** beads, what numbers would you be able to create on an abacus?

**Answer:**

**Marks:** /2

3. What is the greatest number of beads that can be placed on **(a)** the tens line and **(b)** the units line?

**Answers:** (a) (b) **Marks:** /3



**Today's Marks:** /6

## Day Two Try these.

CLUES

| 0 | 1 | 2 | 3 | 4 | 5 | 6 | 7 | 8 | 9 |
|---|---|---|---|---|---|---|---|---|---|

**Team Talk**
- Reader
- Calculator
- Checker
- Reporter

You have a set of digits, 0–9. Can you arrange these digits so that your numbers are as close to the clues below as possible? You can only use each digit **once**.

1. What is the largest two-digit number that can be made using the digits 0–9?

**Joke!**
**SEVEN**
How do you make seven even?
Take away the 's'!

**Answer:** ______ **Marks:** ___ /1

T U

2. What is the smallest two-digit number that can be made using the digits 0–9?

**Answer:** ______ **Marks:** ___ /1

T U

3. What is the largest odd number that can be made using the remaining digits?

**Answer:** ______ **Marks:** ___ /2

T U

4. Write the nearest number to 50 that you can make using the remaining digits.

**Answer:** ______ **Marks:** ___ /3

T U

**Today's Marks:** ___ /7

## Day Three Try these.

| Number | Word | Picture | Place Value |
|---|---|---|---|
| 35 | | | Tens: ______<br>Units: ______<br>Marks: /1 |

| Number | Word | Picture | Place Value |
|---|---|---|---|
| 72 | | | Tens: ______<br>Units: ______<br>Marks: /2 |

3. If you had **6** beads, investigate what numbers you would be able to create on an abacus.

Answer: Marks: /3

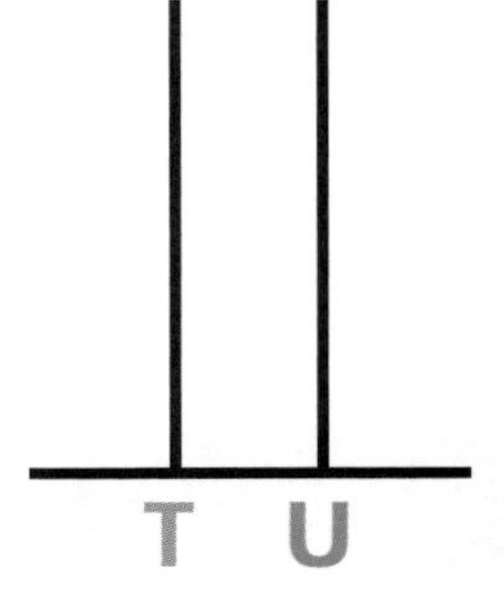




Today's Marks: /6

## Day Four Try these.

1. Céilí has **six tens** and **2 units**. She gets **7** more **units** from the Place Value Fairy. How many tens and units does she have now? Draw your answer.

7 units

Marks: /1

2. Josh has **three tens** and **4 units**. He gets **four** more **tens** from the Place Value Fairy. How many tens and units does he now have? Draw your answer.

Marks: /2

3. Saoirse has **4 tens** and **8 units**. She wants **60 units** in total. How many more tens and units does she need from the Place Value Fairy? Write your answer in expanded form.

Answer: Marks: /3

Today's Marks: /6

## Puzzle power

Two children are playing a game. They need 99 points to win. Colour the two numbers that each must get to reach 99 points.

| Brian already has 30 points. | |
|---|---|
| 40 | 35 |
| 63 | 29 |

| Lana already has 40 points. | |
|---|---|
| 20 | 16 |
| 39 | 48 |

Total Marks: /25

Got this!  Getting there.  Need help! 

I helped my friend by

# 17 Revision 3

## Fairytales

### Day One Try these.

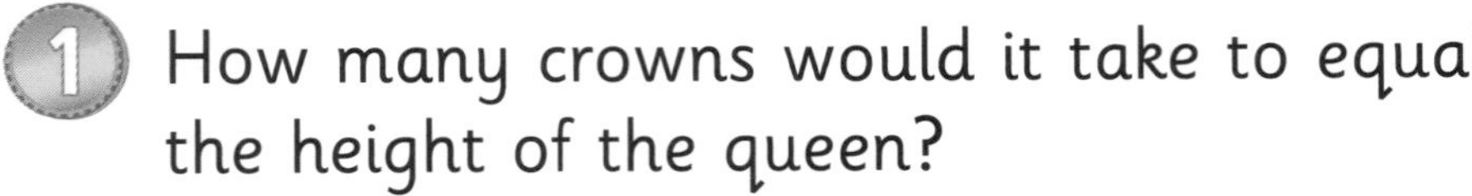

1. How many crowns would it take to equal the height of the queen?

| Answer: | | Marks: | | /1 |
|---|---|---|---|---|

2. How many locks would fit across the castle door?

| Answer: | | Marks: | | /1 |
|---|---|---|---|---|

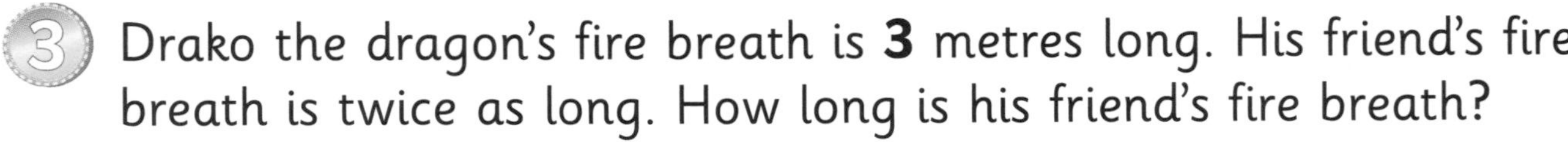

3. Drako the dragon's fire breath is **3** metres long. His friend's fire breath is twice as long. How long is his friend's fire breath?

| Answer: | | Marks: | | /2 |
|---|---|---|---|---|

4. In a castle, tower **A** is **15** metres tall. Tower **B** is **2** metres taller than tower A. Tower **C** is **5** metres shorter than tower A. Put them in order from tallest to shortest.

| Answer: | | Marks: | | /3 |
|---|---|---|---|---|



**Strand:** Measures **Strand Unit:** Length
**Strand:** Number **Strand Units:** Operations – subtraction; Place Value
**Strand:** Shape and Space **Strand Unit:** Spatial Awareness

**Today's Marks:** /7

## Day Two Try these.

16 knights arrived at the castle gates. **12** marched into the castle grounds. How many stayed at the gates?

**Answer:** **Marks:** /1

2. The queen invited **20** guests to a banquet. If only **14** guests turned up, how many did not come?

**Answer:** **Marks:** /1

3. **5** jewels were stolen from the king's throne. If there were **11** jewels to begin with, how many were left?

**Answer:** **Marks:** /2

4. A wicked witch has cast **20** spells on the castle towers. She cast **7** spells on the first and **5** on the second. How many spells did she cast on the third tower?

**Answer:** **Marks:** /3

**Today's Marks:** /7

## Day Three Try these.

1. The prince is standing first in a line, holding a glass slipper. Cinderella is standing between her fairy godmother and her stepmother. Where are they all standing in the line? Draw them.

Marks: /1

2. The king's crown has rolled **underneath** the throne. His cane is lying **across** the two arm rests. On **top** of the throne are his glasses. Draw all of them.

Marks: /1

3. Colour the area below the belt **blue**. Colour the right shoulder **red** and the left shoulder **green**. Colour the area above the belt **orange**.

Marks: /2

4. 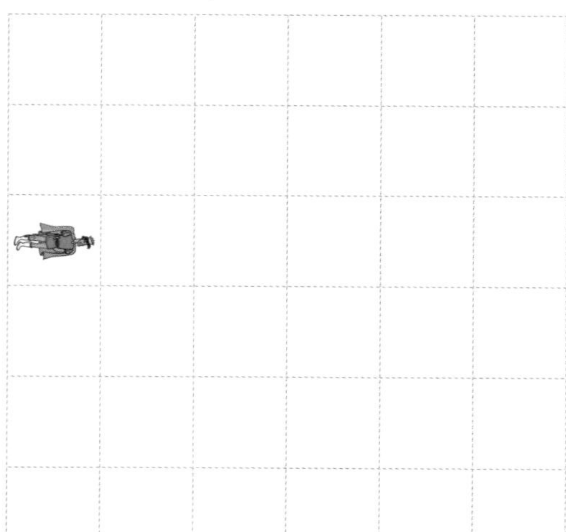

The prince is standing in his hallway. He walks straight for 2 squares and turns right. He walks straight for 3 squares, turns right and walks one square. Mark where he ends up.

Marks: /3



Today's Marks: /7

## Day Four Try these.

CLUES

1 The queen had **23** ball gowns and she bought **4** more. How many ball gowns does she have now in total? Record your answer on the abacus.

T U

| Answer: | | Marks: | | /1 |
|---|---|---|---|---|

2 The king is in the counting house, counting all of his money. Ring the purses with the digit **3** in the **tens** place.

| Marks: | | /2 |
|---|---|---|

3 Each of the queen's gowns has a number and she has a pair of gloves that adds up to this number. Match the correct pair of gloves to each gown by colouring them the same colour.

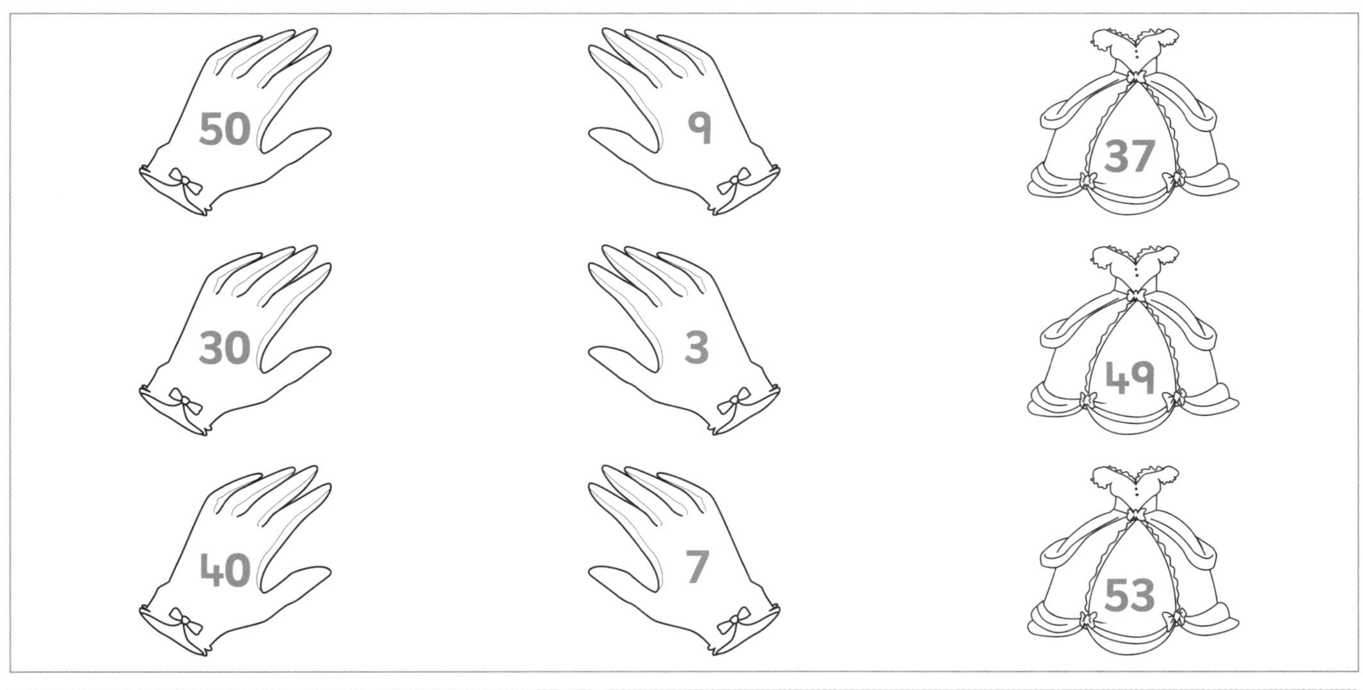


| Answer: | | Marks: | | /3 |
|---|---|---|---|---|

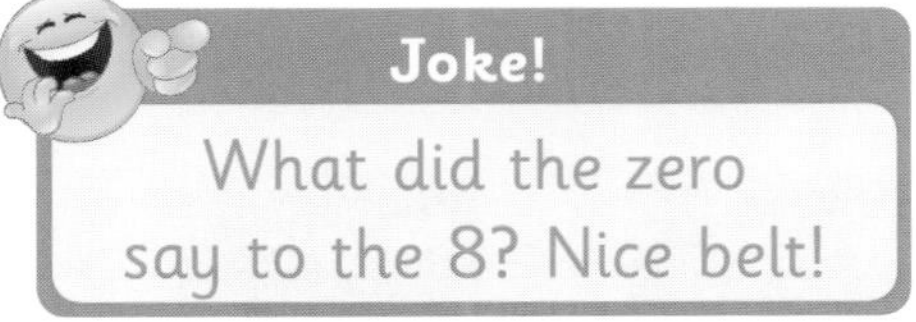


| Today's Marks: | | /6 |
|---|---|---|

| Total Marks: | | /27 |
|---|---|---|

# 18 Strategy: Simplifying

## Day One

The strategy of simplifying is helpful when a number story seems too difficult at first. It helps you to break down the number story, so that you can work out how to solve the puzzle. Using smaller numbers or changing the language into words that you know will help you a lot.

**Try these.**

1. Two workers can make **2** dolls in **2** days. How many dolls can the two workers make in **6** days?

| Answer: | | Marks: | | /1 |
|---|---|---|---|---|

2. Davina invites her two cousins to her house. Her cousins invite **2** friends each. How many guests will be coming to Davina's house?

| Answer: | | Marks: | | /1 |
|---|---|---|---|---|

3. Suzy has **3** dogs. Each dog has two puppies. How many dogs and puppies does Suzy have in total?

| Answer: | | Marks: | | /2 |
|---|---|---|---|---|

4. Roy, Ger and Shane are holding a tennis league. They each need to play a match with every other boy until there is one winner. How many matches will they play in total?

| Answer: | | Marks: | | /3 |
|---|---|---|---|---|

Today's Marks: /7

## Day Two Try these.

CLUES

**1** Imagine that you have **4 pink** counters, **4 purple** counters and **4 orange** counters. Use crayons to draw the counters on the grid, but counters of the same colour cannot be placed above, below or next to each other.

| | | | |
|---|---|---|---|
| | | | |
| | | | |
| | | | |

Marks: /1

**2** Share **15** sausages between the children and Cody the dog. If each child gets **two**, how many does Cody get?

Answer: Marks: /1

**3** In a secret code, the letters of the alphabet stand for numbers. The word 'bee' is worth 12 points and the word 'dog' is worth 26 points. What is the word '**cat**' worth?

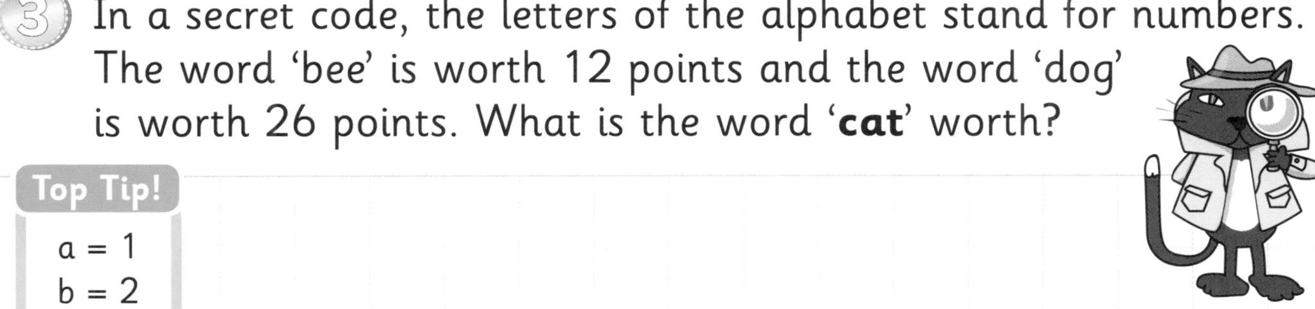

**Top Tip!**

a = 1
b = 2
c = 3

Answer: Marks: /2

**4** Between **1** and **50**, there are four numbers in which the tens digit is half of the units digit. Find the four numbers.

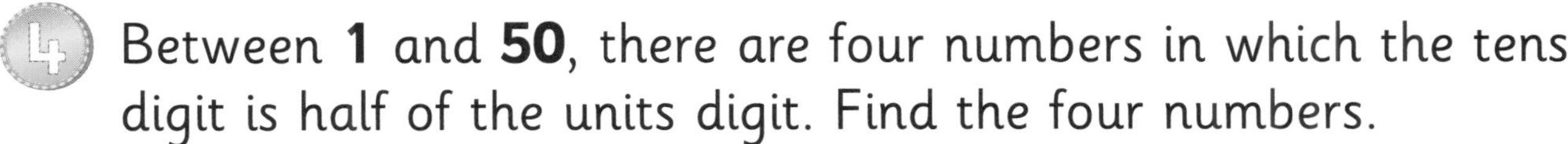

Answer: Marks: /3

## Day Three Try these.

CLUES

1. If 1 was 3, 2 was 4 and 3 was 5, what would 2 + 3 equal?

Answer: Marks: /1

2. Jody writes down the numbers from 1 to 30. How many times does she write the digit **3**?

Answer: Marks: /1

3. Lucas shoots **3** arrows at the target and scores the highest possible score. What is it?

3
7
10

Answer: Marks: 2

4. How many rulers would be the same length as **12** pencils?

Answer: Marks: /3



Today's Marks: /7

## Day Four Try these.

1. The Little Mermaid has found a number between 16 and 30 of pretty shells on the seabed. When she puts them in groups of **five**, there are **4** left over. When she puts them in groups of **three**, there are **2** left over. How many shells does she have?

**Answer:** **Marks:** /1

2. Joe and Benny play squash. Last week, Benny played **3** more games than Joe. If they played **11** games in total between them, how many games did they each play?

**Answer:** **Marks:** /2

3. Miss Barry drinks **16** cups of tea in total each week. On weekend days, she drinks **4** more cups than she does on weekdays (Monday to Friday). How many cups does she drink **(a)** on Wednesday and **(b)** on Sunday?

**Answers:** (a) (b) **Marks:** /3

**Today's Marks:** /6

**Total Marks:** /27 Got this!  Getting there.  Need help! 

I loved doing

# 19 Weight

**We are learning to:** Investigate weight using non-standard and standard units. ☐
Use appropriate non-standard measuring units and instruments. ☐
Investigate weight using standard units (kilograms). ☐

## Day One Look at the example below.

How many erasers equal the weight of an empty beaker?

CLUES

**Circle the numbers and keywords:**
erasers, weight, beaker

**Link with operation needed (+ or –):** None

**Use a strategy:** Trial and improvement.

**Estimate and calculate:**

| My estimate: more than 10 | Try it out using a balance. Count the erasers. | **Answer:** 12 |
|---|---|---|

**Summarise how you got your answer:**
I counted how many erasers equalled the weight of a beaker.

**Try these.**

CLUES

1. If you had **(a)** a pencil case full of coins and **(b)** a pencil case full of stickers, which pencil case would weigh more?

**Answer:** **Marks:** /1

2. Name some items in the classroom that are heavier than a school bag. Explain your answer.

**Answer:** **Marks:** /2

3. Name some items in the classroom that are lighter than a laptop. Explain your answer.

**Answer:** **Marks:** /3



**Today's Marks:** /6

## Day Two Try these.

1. I have a balance. There are **10** cubes on one side and **5** cubes on the other side. How many **more** cubes do I need to balance the scales?

| Answer: | | Marks: | | /1 |
|---|---|---|---|---|

**Top Tip!**

**How does a balance work?**

It is like a see-saw. The heavier side goes down and the lighter side goes up.

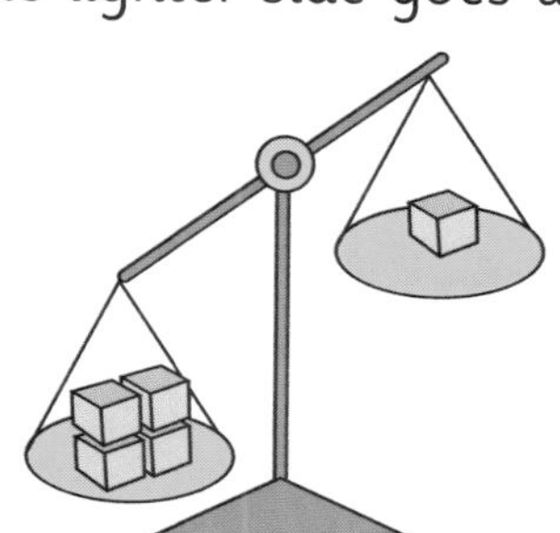

2. If there are **12** cubes on one side and **20** cubes on the other side, how many **less** do I need to balance the scales?

| Answer: | | Marks: | | /1 |
|---|---|---|---|---|

3. I use **25** cubes to balance my copy and pencil together. I need only **6** cubes to balance just my pencil. How many cubes would I need to balance just my copy?

| Answer: | | Marks: | | /2 |
|---|---|---|---|---|

4. If it takes **6** cubes to balance **1** pencil, how many cubes would I need to balance **3** pencils?

| Answer: | | Marks: | | /3 |
|---|---|---|---|---|

| Today's Marks: | | /7 |
|---|---|---|

## Day Three Try these.

CLUES

**Team Talk**

Reader
Calculator
Checker
Reporter

1. The vet examined Cora's sick puppy yesterday. Its weight was **12** kg. This was **2** kg lighter than last month's weight. What was the puppy's weight last month?

12kg

**Answer:** **Marks:** /1

2. At a garden centre, there are two bags of compost. One bag weighs **4** kg and the other weighs **9** kg. How heavy are the two bags together?

**Answer:** **Marks:** /1

3. A weightlifter at a CrossFit event lifted **2** weights of **10** kg each. If a **5** kg weight had been added to each side of the bar, what total weight would he have lifted then?

10 kg 10 kg

**Answer:** **Marks:** /2

4. At the post office, parcels are weighed to work out the cost of delivery. Tara had one parcel weighing **22** kg and another parcel that was **3** kg heavier. How much did they weigh in total?

**Answer:** **Marks:** /3



**Today's Marks:** /7

## Day Four Try these.

1. A playschool got a delivery of sand. The trailer contained **80** kg of sand when it arrived at the playschool and just **60** kg of sand when it left. How much sand did the playschool get?

Answer: Marks: /1

2. Ryanair allow each passenger to carry one cabin bag weighing up to **10** kg onboard a flight for free. If my bag weighs **16** kg, how many kilograms will I have to pay for?

Answer: Marks: /2

3. Three sisters ordered coal. Jane ordered **50** kg. Sarah ordered **5** kg less than Jane and Kate ordered **5** kg more than Jane. Write the weights ordered from lightest to heaviest.

Answer:

Marks: /3

## Super Sleuth investigates

Today's Marks: /6

Write the weight above each scales.

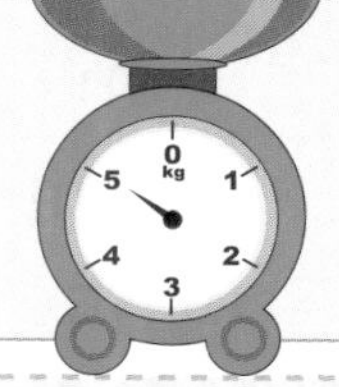

Total Marks: /26

Got this!  Getting there.  Need help! 

I would like to get better at

# 20 Fractions

**We are learning to:** Establish and identify half of sets to 20. ☐

## Day One Look at the example below.

10 children go to a dance class. $\frac{1}{2}$ of the children walk to the class. How many children walk to the class?

**C**ircle the numbers and keywords: 10, $\frac{1}{2}$ of the children

**L**ink with operation needed (+ or –): None

**U**se a strategy: Draw a picture.

**E**stimate and calculate:

| My estimate: less than 10 | $\frac{1}{2}$ of 10 = 5 | **Answer:** 5 |
|---|---|---|

**S**ummarise how you got your answer:
$\frac{1}{2}$ means splitting into 2 equal parts. I split 10 into 2 groups of 5.

**Try these.**

1. A butcher made **12** meat pies and sold $\frac{1}{2}$. How many does he have left?

   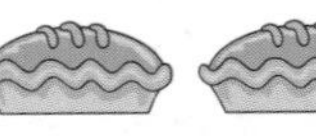 

**Answer:** ______ **Marks:** ___ /1

2. These coins show Rebecca and Darren's combined pocket money. How much do they each get?

**Answer:** ______ **Marks:** ___ /2

3. Sonya found **€10** in her jeans pocket and another **€4** in her jacket pocket. If she spent **half** of this money, how much does she have left?

**Answer:** ______ **Marks:** ___ /3



**Today's Marks:** ___ /6

## Day Two Try these.

1. There are **20** pages in Matthew's homework copy. He has used $\frac{1}{2}$ of the copy. How many pages has he used?

**Answer:** | **Marks:** /1

**Top Tip!**

Halving a number means splitting it into 2 equal parts.

One whole — One half — One half

2. If you can fill **16** cups from a full bottle of juice, how many cups can you fill from $\frac{1}{2}$ a bottle of juice?

**Answer:** | **Marks:** /1

3. There are **18** puppets in a basket in a shop. $\frac{1}{2}$ of them are zoo animals and the other $\frac{1}{2}$ are farm animals. How many zoo animal puppets are there?

**Answer:** | **Marks:** /2

4. Kim had **6** counters and Kelly had **4** counters. They played a game and ended up with equal amounts. How many do they each have now?

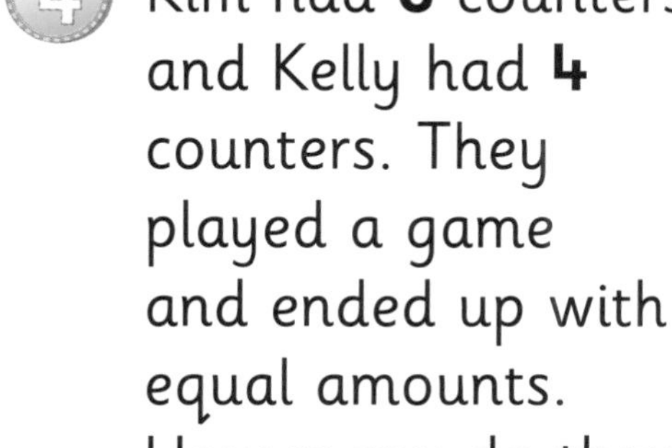

**Answer:** | **Marks:** /3

**Today's Marks:** /7

## Day Three Try these.

## Super Sleuth challenge

Complete the ladybirds below and use them to help you halve numbers. Remember: Both sides need to be equal.

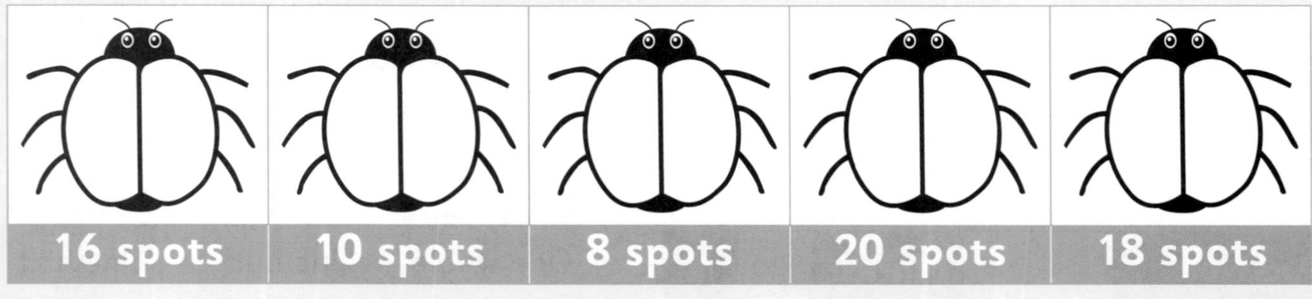


1. José had a carton of **6** eggs, but he dropped it and half of them broke. How many eggs were left?

Answer: Marks: /1

2. Tiago has **8** sweets and Rowan has **6** sweets. Can you think of a way that they could have equal amounts?

Answer: Marks: /1

3. Martin played **half** the amount of games on his tablet that Ely played. If Ely played **12** games, how many did Martin play?

Answer: Marks: /2

4. At a quiz, there were **20** questions. Team 1 got **half** of the questions right. How many questions did they get right?

Answer: Marks: /3



Today's Marks: /7

## Day Four Try these.

CLUES

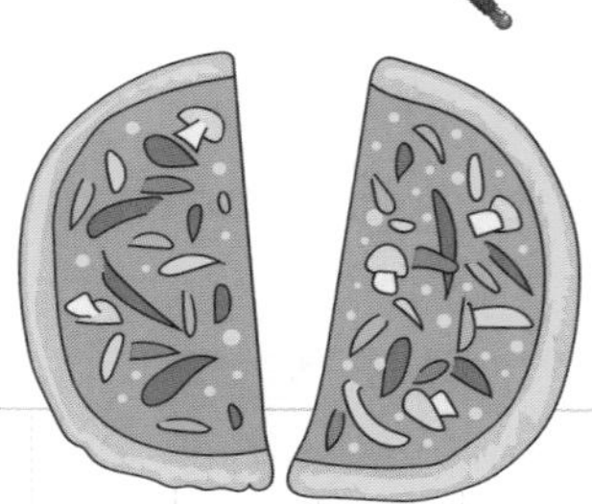

1. If you invited **5** guests to a party, how many pizzas would you need to cook so that you and each of your guests could have $\frac{1}{2}$ a pizza each?

**Answer:** **Marks:** /1

2. Samuel practises piano every day for $\frac{1}{2}$ an hour. For how many hours does he practise altogether in **4** days?

**Answer:** **Marks:** /2

3. Lebron saved up **€20**. He spent **half** of it on a basketball. He then spent **half** of the change on a magazine. How much money does he have left?

**Answer:** **Marks:** /3

**Today's Marks:** /6

### Super Sleuth challenge

Colour half of the group of squares in each pattern.

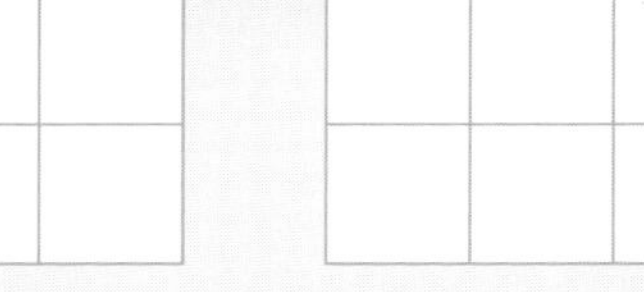

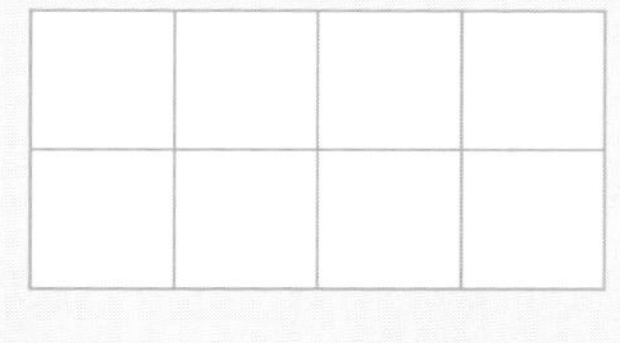

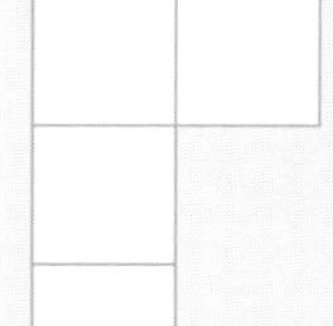

**Total Marks:** /26

**Got this!**  **Getting there.** 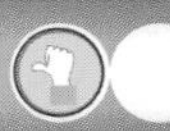 **Need help!** 

**I enjoyed**

# 21 Operations 1

**We are learning to:** Add or subtract numbers, without and with renaming, within 99. ☐ Estimate differences. ☐ Explore repeated addition and group counting. ☐

**Day One** Look at the example below.

Michaela borrowed 10 books from the library. If she read 1 book each night, how many had she left to read after a week?

**C**ircle the numbers and keywords: 10 books, a week

**L**ink with operation needed (+ or –): Subtract (–).

**U**se a strategy:
Draw a picture. 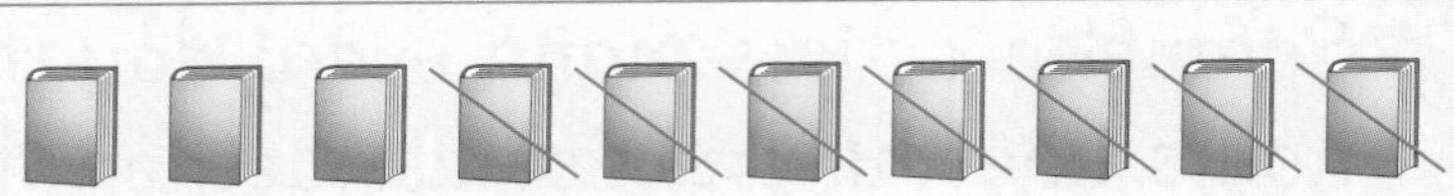

**E**stimate and calculate:
My estimate: less than 10 | 10 – 7 = 3 | **Answer:** 3

**S**ummarise how you got your answer:
There are 7 days in a week, so I took 7 away from 10.

Try these.

1. A DVD costs **€18** and a board game costs **€21**. How much do they cost in total?

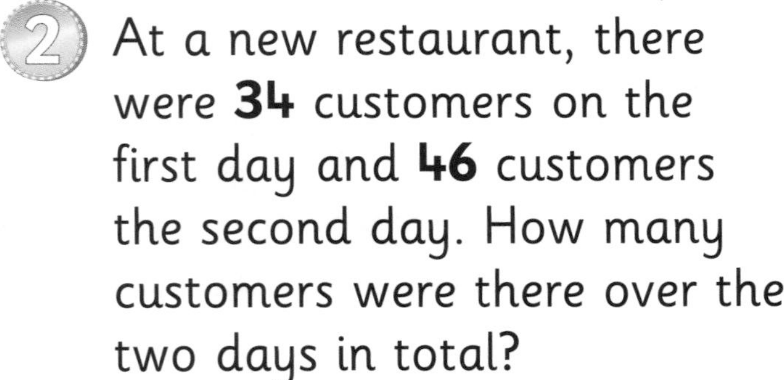

2. At a new restaurant, there were **34** customers on the first day and **46** customers the second day. How many customers were there over the two days in total?

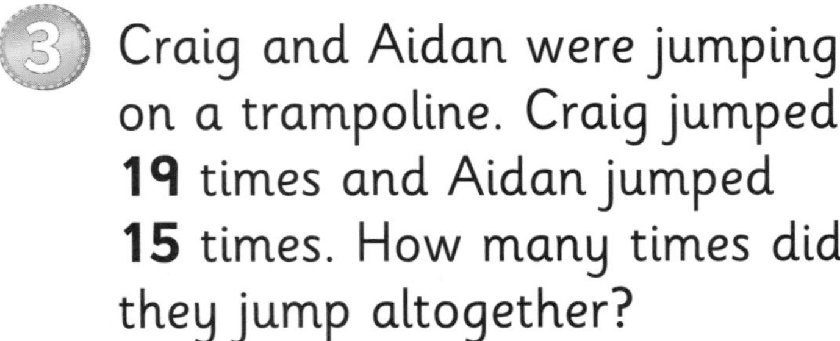

3. Craig and Aidan were jumping on a trampoline. Craig jumped **19** times and Aidan jumped **15** times. How many times did they jump altogether?

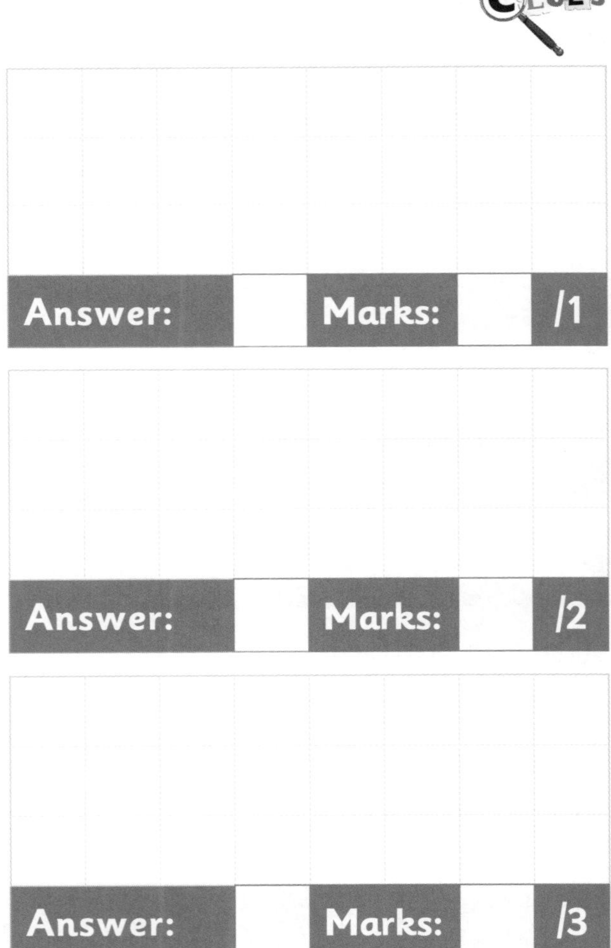


Today's Marks: /6

## Day Two Try these.

**Team Talk**

- Reader
- Calculator
- Checker
- Reporter

1. **15** guests have been invited to a birthday party. How many more guests need to be invited to make a total of **29**?

**Answer:** **Marks:** /1

2. Karl made a playlist of **57** songs. If **35** of them were fast songs, how many of them were slow songs?

**Answer:** **Marks:** /1

3. Fiadh is collecting stamps to get a free pie dish from the supermarket. So far, she has collected **24** stamps. If she needs a total of **39**, how many more does she need to collect?

Collect **39** stamps

**Answer:** **Marks:** /2

4. A sports shop got a delivery of **87** golf balls on Monday morning. By Wednesday evening, there were **64** left. How many golf balls had been sold by Wednesday evening?

**Answer:** **Marks:** /3

### Puzzle power

Think of a number. Now, double it. Now, add 6. Halve the number. Finally, subtract the number that you started with. The answer is 3! Try this out using different numbers.

**Today's Marks:** /7

## Day Three Try these.

1. Milly's Bakery made **28** sausage rolls in the morning and **31** in the afternoon. How many did they make altogether?

| Answer: | | Marks: | /1 |
|---|---|---|---|

2. There were **68** children in a swimming pool, but **23** got out. How many were left in the pool?

| Answer: | | Marks: | /2 |
|---|---|---|---|

3. Sylvia blew up **24** balloons. Her brother Timothy blew up a further **38** balloons. How many balloons were there?

| Answer: | | Marks: | /3 |
|---|---|---|---|

## Have a go!

Can you mentally subtract 12 from each of these numbers?

Can you mentally subtract 13 from each of these numbers?

| Take away 12. | | |
|---|---|---|
| 32 | → | |
| 25 | → | |
| 36 | → | |
| 23 | → | |

| Take away 13. | | |
|---|---|---|
| 33 | → | |
| 29 | → | |
| 35 | → | |
| 24 | → | |



Today's Marks: /6

## Day Four Try these.

CLUES

**Team Talk**

Reader
Calculator
Checker
Reporter

1. Arrange the digits **1**, **3**, **5** and **7** in the squares so that the sum is correct. Can you think of a number story?

   − □□ / □□ = 2 6

   Marks: /1

2. Using the digits **2**, **4**, **6** and **8**, subtract the **smallest** two-digit number that you can make from the **largest** two-digit number that you can make.

   − □□ / □□

   Marks: /2

3. Think of the smallest two-digit, **odd** number that it is possible to make. Subtract this number from the largest two-digit, **even** number that it is possible to make.

   − □□ / □□

   Marks: /3

Today's Marks: /6

### Puzzle power

Can you arrange the digits **5**, **6**, **7** and **8** in the circles so that the difference between two touching circles is always greater than 1?

Total Marks: /25

Got this! Getting there. Need help!

My favourite activity was

# 22  Time 2

**We are learning to:** Use the vocabulary of time to sequence events. ☐
Read days, dates and months using a calendar. ☐

## Day One Look at the example below.

If it is June now and Callan's birthday is in October, how many months will he have to wait?

**C**ircle the numbers and keywords:
June, October, how many months

**L**ink with operation needed (+ or –): None

**U**se a strategy: Act it out.

**E**stimate and calculate:

| My estimate: less than 6 months | Count on from June to October. | **Answer:** 4 months |
|---|---|---|

**S**ummarise how you got your answer:
I counted on from June to October.

### Try these.

1. Name the **2nd** month of the year. Can you think of any special dates in this month?

**Answer:** Marks: /1

2. In **November**, Miriam and her family booked a summer holiday at the seaside. If their holiday is in **8** months' time, during which month will they go?

**Answer:** Marks: /2

3. Stephanie's hip-hop group will march in the Saint Patrick's Day parade. If they start practising **5 months ahead**, in which month will they start?

**Answer:** Marks: /3



Today's Marks: /6

## Day Two Try these.

This month is ____________.

Fill in the correct dates for this month. (You can write '1, 2, 3', etc. for short.)

**Rhyme**

30 days have September, April, June and November. All the rest have 31, except for February alone, which has 28 days clear and 29 in each leap year.

| Monday | Tuesday | Wednesday | Thursday | Friday | Saturday | Sunday |
|---|---|---|---|---|---|---|
| | | | | | | |
| | | | | | | |
| | | | | | | |
| | | | | | | |
| | | | | | | |
| | | | | | | |

1. On which day does the 1st of the month fall?

**Answer:** **Marks:** /1

2. How many Mondays and Fridays are there in total this month?

**Answer:** **Marks:** /1

3. If you could add **2** more days to this month, how many days would there be?

**Answer:** **Marks:** /2

4. What day and date will it be one week from today?

**Answer:** **Marks:** /3

**Today's Marks:** /7

## Day Three Try these.

| January | | | | | | |
|---|---|---|---|---|---|---|
| **Monday** | **Tuesday** | **Wednesday** | **Thursday** | **Friday** | **Saturday** | **Sunday** |
| | | | | | | 1 New Year's Day |
| 2 | 3 | 4 World Braille Day | 5 | 6 | 7 | 8 |
| 9 Writing Competition | 10 | 11 BT Young Scientist Exhibition | 12 BT Young Scientist Exhibition | 13 BT Young Scientist Exhibition | 14 BT Young Scientist Exhibition | 15 |
| 16 Martin Luther King Day | 17 | 18 World Day of the Snowman | 19 | 20 | 21 | 22 |
| 23 | 24 Share a Compliment Day | 25 | 26 Australia Day | 27 | 28 Chinese New Year begins | 29 |
| 30 Storytelling Week begins | 31 Backwards Day | | | | | |

1. On what day and date was Australia Day celebrated?

**Answer:** **Marks:** /1

2. Find an event that lasted for 4 days and give the dates on which it took place.

**Answer:** **Marks:** /1

3. From Backwards Day, count back how many sleeps ago the Chinese New Year began.

**Answer:** **Marks:** /2

4. On the 17th, how many days away was Share a Compliment Day?

**Answer:** **Marks:** /3



**Today's Marks:** /7

## Day Four Try these.

1. Can you name the months of autumn? Ring the one that has only 30 days.

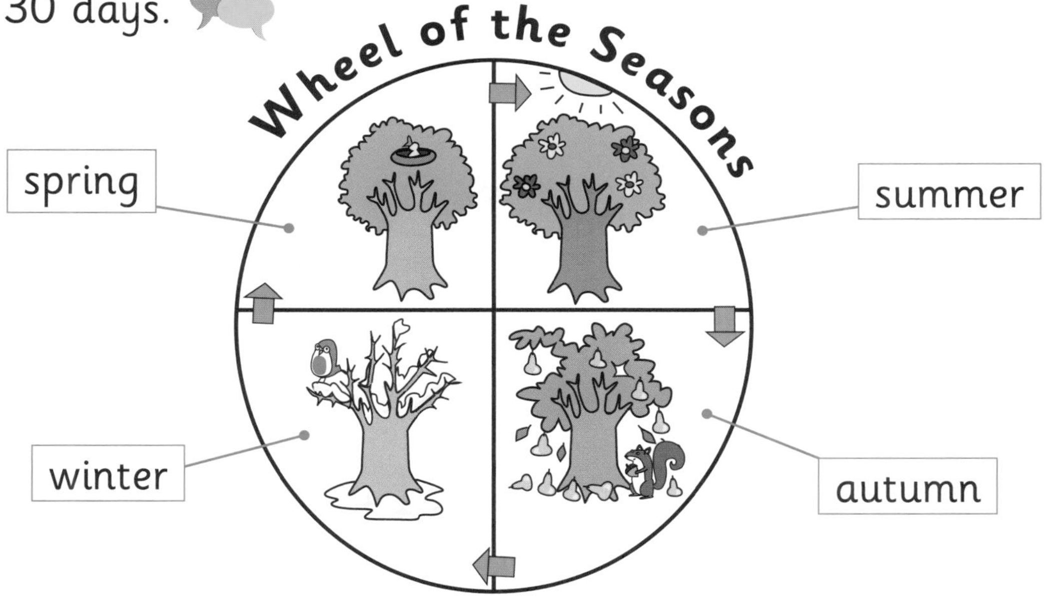


**Answer:** | **Marks:** /1

2. In which season is the shortest month of the year? How many days does it have? Explain.

**Answer:** | **Marks:** /2

3. The first and last months of the year are in which season? Can you name the other month in this season?

**Answer:** | **Marks:** /3

## Super Sleuth investigates

**Today's Marks:** /6

Colour the days yellow and the months **purple**.

| Sunday | June | Saturday | April | January |
|---|---|---|---|---|
| October | August | July | Thursday | Tuesday |
| Friday | December | May | Wednesday | March |
| September | Monday | February | November | |

**Total Marks:** /26 **Got this!**  **Getting there.**  **Need help!** 

**I helped my friend by**

# 23 Revision 4

## The Toy Show

### Day One Try these.

1. Which toy do you think is heaviest, a box of wooden blocks or a board game?

Answer: Marks: /1

2. Which wheeled toy do you think is heaviest: the skateboard, the bicycle, the scooter or the rollerblades?

Answer: Marks: /1

3. At the Toy Show, two displays like those shown below were made with **1 kg** tubs of Play-Doh. How many kilograms of Play-Doh were there in total in the two displays?

Answer: Marks: /2

4. A remote-controlled car weighs **2 kg**. If my aunt bought **3** for her children, how heavy was her shopping bag?

Answer: Marks: /3



Strand: Measures Strand Units: Weight; Time
Strand: Number Strand Units: Fractions; Operations

Today's Marks: /7

## Day Two Try these.

**Top Tip!** Act it out.

CLUES

1 Half of these lights over the stage were turned off. How many were turned off?

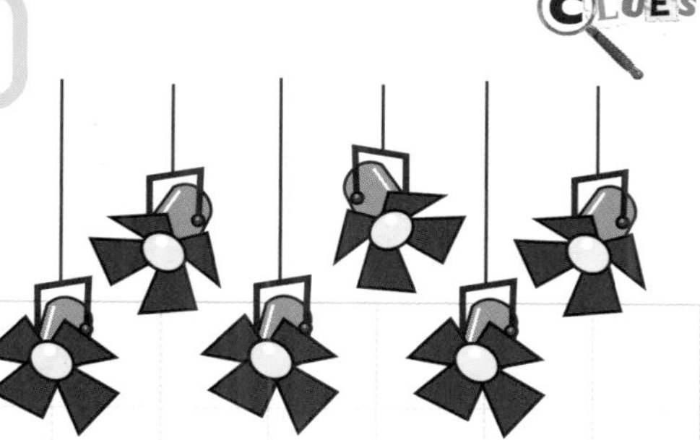

**Answer:** **Marks:** /1

2 These camera operators work on the stage. If $\frac{1}{2}$ of them go on a tea break, how many are left?

**Answer:** **Marks:** /1

3 This image shows $\frac{1}{2}$ of the microphones used on the stage. How many microphones were used in total?

**Answer:** **Marks:** /2

4 $\frac{1}{2}$ of the **10** dancers and $\frac{1}{2}$ of the **20** singers at the Toy Show won a goodie bag. How many people won a goodie bag?

**Answer:** **Marks:** /3

**Today's Marks:** /7

## Day Three Try these.

**Top Tip!**
Simplify.

1. Among the audience, **39** people wore a jester hat and **7** people wore a top hat. How many people wore a hat in total?

Answer: Marks: /1

2. Among the audience, **65** people were given a food hamper and **9** people were given a toy hamper. How many hampers were given out?

Answer: Marks: /1

3. **89** members of the audience bought a raffle ticket and **10** of them won a spot prize. How many did **not** win a spot prize?

Answer: Marks: /2

4. **3** scouts arrived at the Toy Show early and they took their seats. **15** more scouts arrived a little later and they also took their seats. Suddenly, **10** of the scouts hurried off to the toilet before the show began. How many scouts were still in their seats?

Answer: Marks: /3



Today's Marks: /7

## Day Four Try these.

| December | | | | | | |
|---|---|---|---|---|---|---|
| Monday | Tuesday | Wednesday | Thursday | Friday | Saturday | Sunday |
| | | | 1 | 2 | 3 | |
| 5 | 6 | | 8 | 9 | 10 | 11 |
| 12 | 13 | 14 | 15 | | 17 | 18 |
| | 20 | | 22 | 23 | 24 | 25 |
| 26 | 27 | 28 | 29 | 30 | 31 | |

**Team Talk**

Reader

Calculator

Checker

Reporter

1. Write the missing dates in the calendar above.

Marks: /1

2. On December **13th**, how many more days is it until Christmas Day?

Answer: Marks: /2

3. What date is it **2** weeks after December **15th**?

Answer: Marks: /3

**Joke!**

What is a frog's favourite year?

A leap year!

Today's Marks: /6

Total Marks: /27

# 24 Strategy: Make a Table

## Day One

Making a table helps you to organise a number story by listing the facts in rows and columns. This strategy can also help you to check your work by seeing it clearly laid out.

Try these.

1. Denis raced his **blue**, **red** and **green** tractors. What different ways could they have finished?

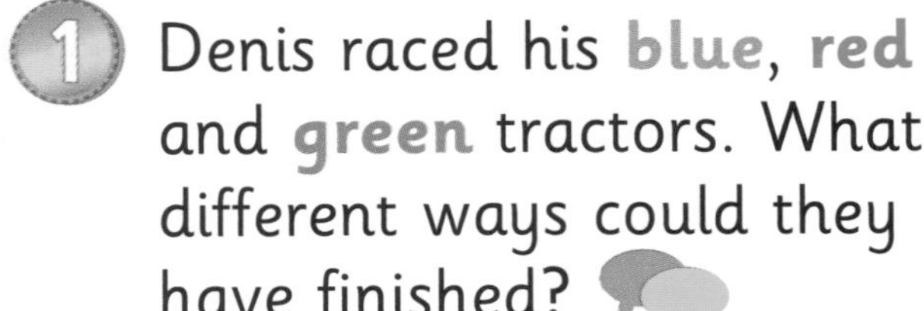

| 1st Place | 2nd Place | 3rd Place |
|---|---|---|
| | | |
| | | |
| | | |

Marks: /1

2. **Chip**, **Ralph**, **Snoopy** and **Ted** are in a dog show. How many different ways can they finish?

| 1st Place | 2nd Place | 3rd Place | 4th Place |
|---|---|---|---|
| | | | |
| | | | |
| | | | |
| | | | |

Marks: /2

3. Jocelynn has a bag of Skittles. For every **green** Skittle, she has **3 red** Skittles. If she has **3 green** Skittles, how many **red** Skittles does she have?

| Green | 1 | 2 | 3 |
|---|---|---|---|
| Red | 3 | 6 | |
| **Total** | 4 | | |

Answer: Marks: /3



Today's Marks: /6

## Day Two Try these.

1 What two-digit numbers can be made using **6** and **3**?

| Largest number | |
|---|---|
| Smallest number | |

Marks: /1

2 Louise threw two dice and the numbers, when added together, made **8**. What numbers could have landed?

| Die 1 | | | |
|---|---|---|---|
| Die 2 | | | |
| Total | 8 | 8 | 8 |

Marks: /1

**Team Talk**

Reader

Calculator

Checker

Reporter

3 Fabien threw three dice and the numbers, when added together, made **15**. What numbers could have landed?

| Die 1 | | | |
|---|---|---|---|
| Die 2 | | | |
| Die 3 | | | |
| Total | 15 | 15 | 15 |

Marks: /2

4 **10** children are standing in a line. Zayn is last in the line. He decides to skip a few children when the teacher isn't looking. If he skips one at a time and ends up in **fifth** place, how many children does he skip? Use the table to help you.

| | | | | | | | | | |
|---|---|---|---|---|---|---|---|---|---|
| | | | | | | | | | |

Answer: Marks: /3

Today's Marks: /7

## Day Three Try these.

1. At a party, everyone is given a goodie bag of **two** prizes. Make 6 different goodie bags using the items below.

yo-yo  car  crayons  bubbles

| Goodie bag 1 | | |
|---|---|---|
| Goodie bag 2 | | |
| Goodie bag 3 | | |
| Goodie bag 4 | | |
| Goodie bag 5 | | |
| Goodie bag 6 | | |

Marks: /1

2. The items of clothing below must be sorted into two bags for a charity shop. Show one way that you could split them up.

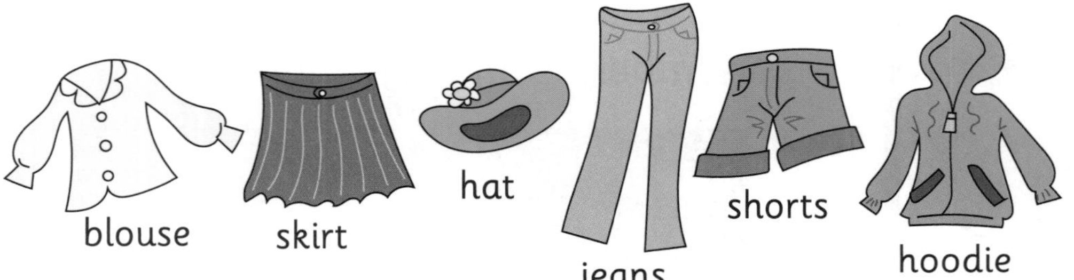


| Bag 1 | | | | | |
|---|---|---|---|---|---|
| Bag 2 | | | | | |

Marks: /2

3. A shop has a meal deal for €5. You get three items – one from each of the menus below. Suggest 3 different meals.

| Sandwich Menu | | | Drink Menu | | | Fruit Menu | | |
|---|---|---|---|---|---|---|---|---|
| bap | roll | wrap | milk | water | juice | apple | banana | pear |

| Meal 1 | | | |
|---|---|---|---|
| Meal 2 | | | |
| Meal 3 | | | |

Marks: /3



Today's Marks: /6

## Day Four Try these.

CLUES

1. Ally and Faye are in an after-school book club. Ally reads **20** pages an hour and Faye reads **10** pages an hour. How many pages will they each have read after three hours?

| | 1 hour | 2 hours | 3 hours | Total |
|---|---|---|---|---|
| Ally | 20 pages | | | |
| Faye | 10 pages | | | |

| Answers: | Ally: | Faye: | Marks: | /1 |
|---|---|---|---|---|

2. Daniel and Zoe both go to the same gym. Daniel goes every **3** days and Zoe goes every **2** days. If they both go on Monday, on what day will they meet next?

| | | | | | | | | |
|---|---|---|---|---|---|---|---|---|
| Daniel | Mon | +3 | Thurs | | | | | |
| Zoe | Mon | +2 | Wed | | | | | |

| Answer: | | Marks: | /2 |
|---|---|---|---|

3. A roller coaster has **9** seats. For every two seats that are filled, one seat is empty. How many **empty** seats are there?

| | | | |
|---|---|---|---|
| Filled | 2 | | |
| Empty | 1 | | |

| Answer: | | Marks: | /3 |
|---|---|---|---|

Today's Marks: /6

Total Marks: /25

Got this!  Getting there.  Need help! 

I loved doing

# 25 Capacity

**We are learning to:** Investigate capacity using standard and non-standard units. ☐
Select and use appropriate measuring units and instruments. ☐

## Day One Look at the example below.

Liz bought 2 cartons of orange juice with 2 litres in each carton. How many litres of juice did she buy altogether?

**Circle the numbers and keywords:** 2 cartons, 2 litres

**Link with operation needed (+ or –):** Add (+).

**Use a strategy:** Draw a picture.

**Estimate and calculate:**

| My estimate: a single-digit answer | 2 + 2 = 4 | **Answer:** 4 litres |
|---|---|---|

**Summarise how you got your answer:**
The 2 cartons contain 2 litres each. I know that 2 + 2 = 4

### Try these.

1. Look at the image. How many cups of tea could you get from **2** identical teapots?

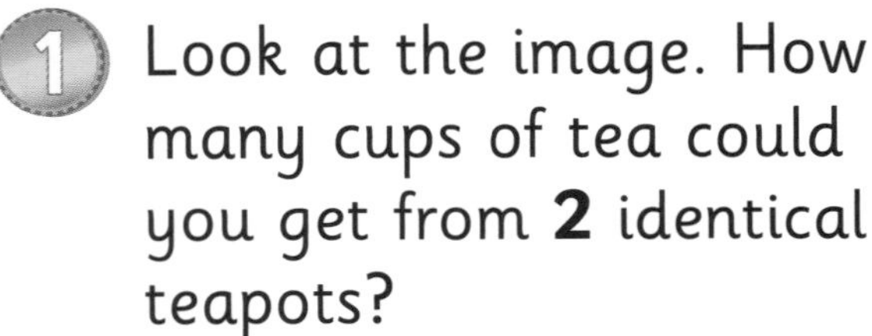

**Answer:** ____ **Marks:** ____ /1

2. **8** glasses of juice can be poured from a full carton. After Henry pours **1** glass, how many more glasses can be poured?

**Answer:** ____ **Marks:** ____ /2

3. Abbey fills her beaker twice a day from a jug of orange. If the jug can fill **4** beakers, how many days will a full jug last her?

**Answer:** ____ **Marks:** ____ /3

**Today's Marks:** ____ /6

## Day Two Try these.

Number the containers in order according to the amount of liquid that they can hold. The container that holds the least amount should be numbered '1'.

| | | | | |
|---|---|---|---|---|
| bath | spoon | barrel | cup | bucket |

Marks: /1

2 Number the glasses in order according to the amount of liquid that they contain. The glass that contains the least amount should be numbered '1'.

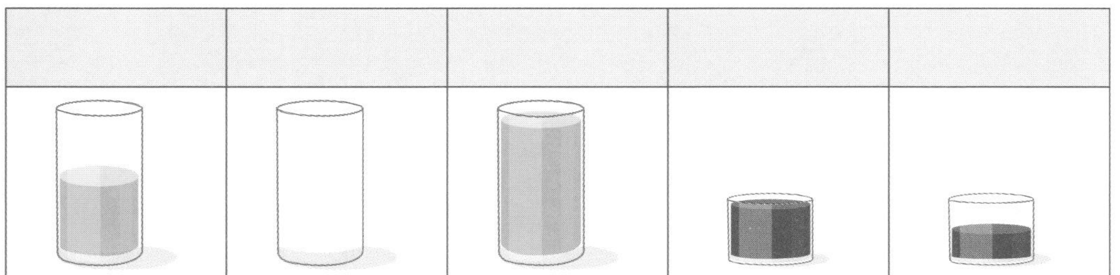

Marks: /1

3 If you had to fill a vase with water, tick (✓) the glass that you would use. How many glasses of water this size do you think it would take to fill a typical vase?

Answer:

Marks: /2

4 Draw and label 4 containers that hold more water than a full glass.

Answer:

Marks: /3

## Day Three Try these.

CLUES

Waldo is busy making potions during his wizard class. Can you help him with the ingredients?

4 litres

2 litres

3 litres

1 litre

5 litres

1. If Waldo has to make a potion of **6 litres** using only **two** ingredients, which two ingredients could he use?

2. If Waldo made a potion using all of the nettle juice and snake oil, how many litres of the potion would there be?

3. If Waldo made a potion using all of the ingredients, how many litres of the potion would there be?

4. Waldo finally made his potion and poured all of it into **7** bottles that held **1** litre each. Which ingredients might he have used in the potion?

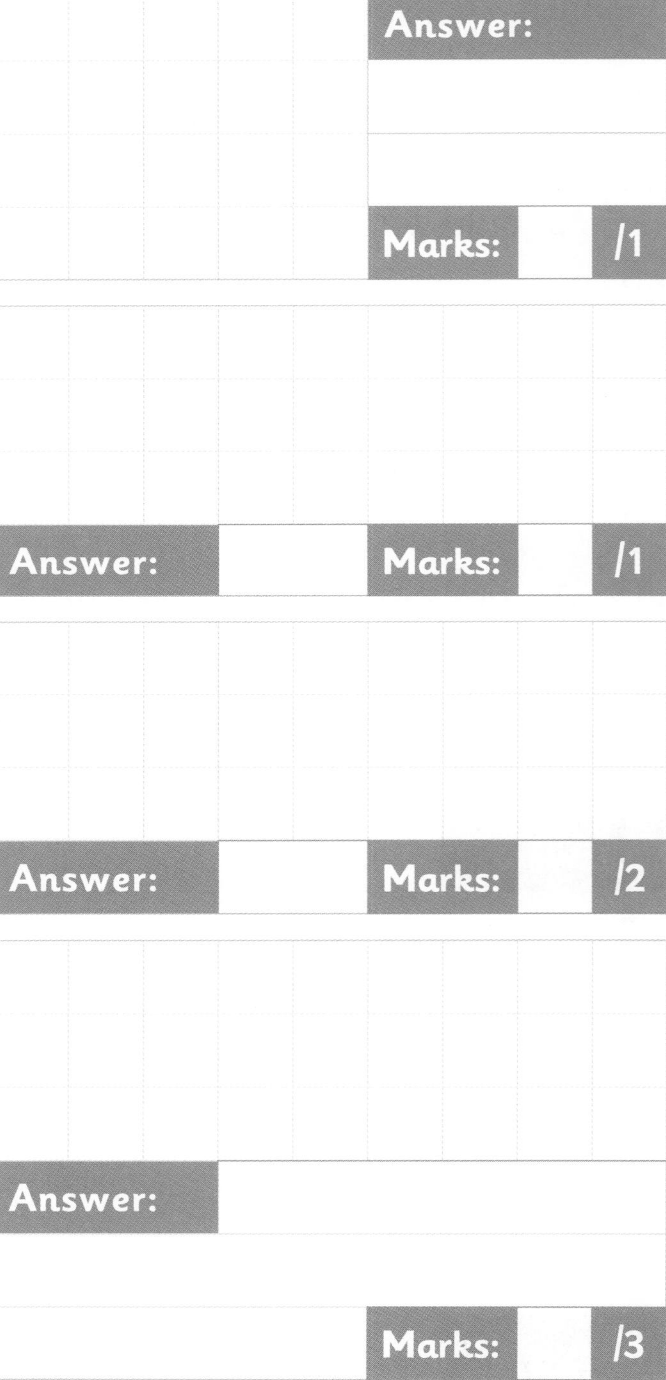




Today's Marks: /7

## Day Four Try these.

1. Label each container as **more than** or **less than** 1 litre and draw two other items of similar capacity.

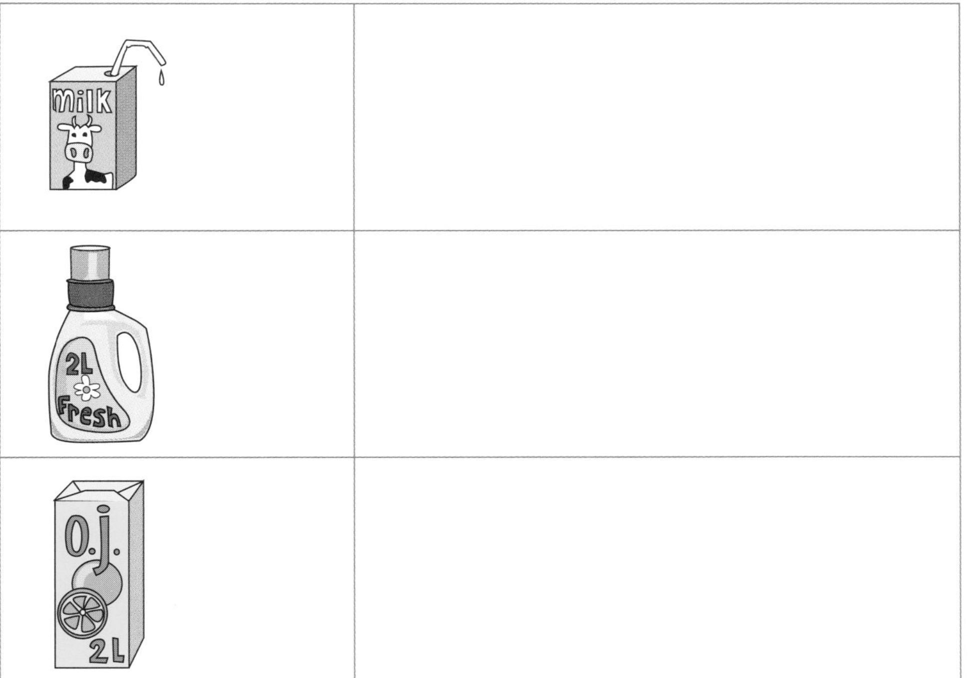

Marks: /1

2. Can you name 3 places where you go to get wet and you will definitely see **more than** 1 litre of water?

Answer: Marks: /2

3. Can you name 4 items from your home that hold **less than** 1 litre of water?

Answer: Marks: /3

Today's Marks: /6

### Puzzle power

What is full of holes, but still holds water?

The **3rd** letter is o. The **4th** letter is n. The **6th** letter is e.

The **1st** letter is s. The **2nd** letter is p. The **5th** letter is g.

Total Marks: /26

Got this!  Getting there.  Need help! 

I would like to get better at

# 26 Extending and Using Patterns

**We are learning to:** Know odd and even numbers. ☐ Use a frame to show the presence of an unknown number. ☐ Use patterns in addition facts. ☐

## Day One Look at the example below.

What shapes come next? ☆ ♥ ♥ ♥ ☆ ♥ ♥ ♥ ☆ ? ? ? ?

CLUES

**Circle the numbers and keywords:** shapes, next

**Link with operation needed (+ or –):** None

**Use a strategy:** Pattern

**Estimate and calculate:**

| My estimate: more hearts than stars | The pattern is 1, 3, 1, 3. | **Answer:** 3 hearts and 1 star |
|---|---|---|

**Summarise how you got your answer:**
I continued the pattern that was already there.

**Try these.**

CLUES

1. Look at the image. There are 9 cubes. 9 is an odd number. If you took 1 cube away, would the number then be odd or even?

**Answer:**

**Marks:** /1

2. Investigate! **(a)** When you add two odd numbers, do you get an odd or an even number? **(b)** When you add two even numbers, do you get an odd or an even number? Explain your answers.

**Answers:** (a)
(b)

**Marks:** /2



**Today's Marks:** /3

## Day Two Try these.

1. Miss Grace gave out **5** stickers on Monday, **10** stickers on Tuesday and **15** stickers on Wednesday. If the pattern continued, how many stickers do you think she gave out on Thursday?

Answer: Marks: /1

2. Joshua lined up his toy cars in three rows. There were **10** in the first row, **10** in the second row and **10** in the third row. How many cars did he have altogether?

Answer: Marks: /2

3. Daddy got **2** text messages at 1 o'clock, **12** text messages at 3 o'clock and **22** text messages at 5 o'clock. If the pattern continued, how many did he get at 7 o'clock? (Hint: Look at the tens values.)

Answer: Marks: /3

### Puzzle power

Finish each pattern by drawing the correct number of dots in the grey section.

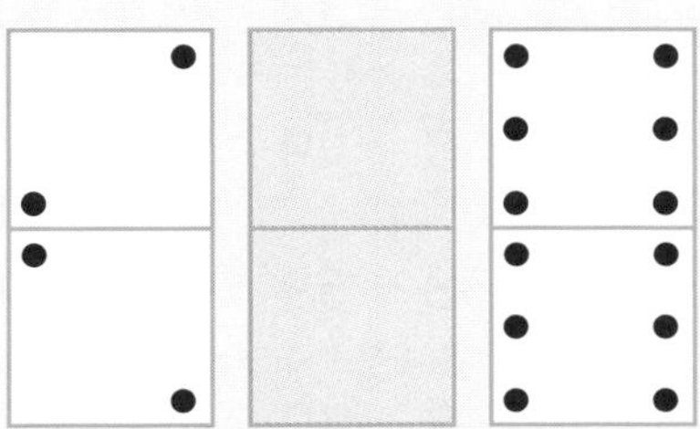

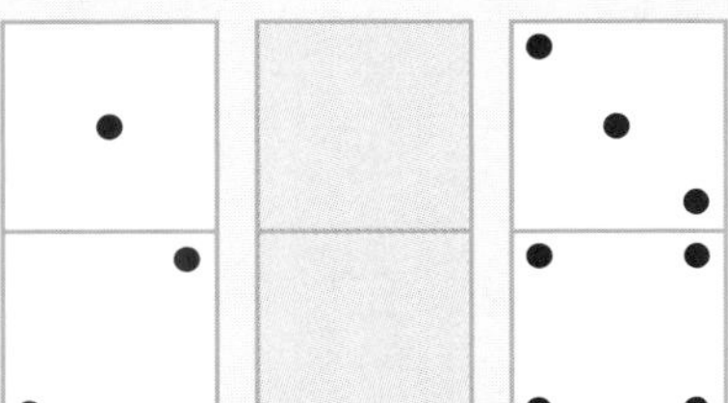

**Joke!**

What is a maths teacher's favourite season?

Sum-mer!

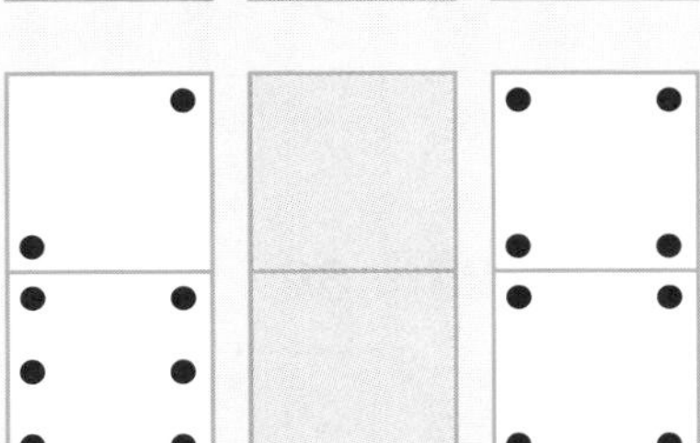

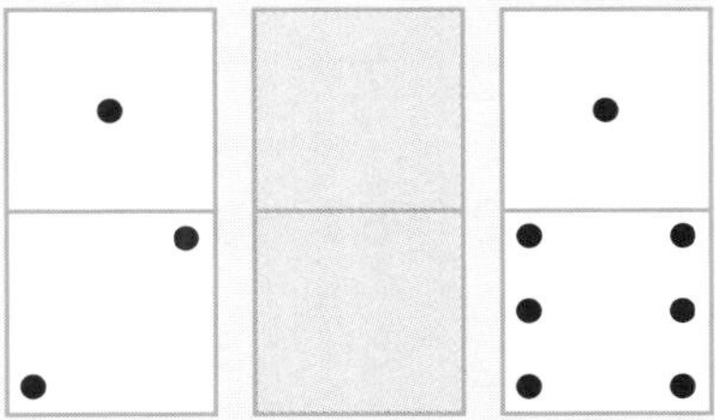

Today's Marks: /6

## Day Three Try these.

There are 10 children in a swimming pool. Break them up into two groups using different number patterns. Use the number strip below to help you.

| 1 | 2 | 3 | 4 | 5 | 6 | 7 | 8 | 9 | 10 |
|---|---|---|---|---|---|---|---|---|---|
| one | two | three | four | five | six | seven | eight | nine | ten |

**Answer:** **Marks:** /1

**2** There are 20 buns on a plate. Break them up into two groups using different number patterns. Use the number box to help you.

| 1 | 2 | 3 | 4 | 5 |
|---|---|---|---|---|
| 6 | 7 | 8 | 9 | 10 |
| 11 | 12 | 13 | 14 | 15 |
| 16 | 17 | 18 | 19 | 20 |

**Answer:**

**Marks:** /2

| 1 | 2 | 3 | 4 | 5 | 6 | 7 | 8 | 9 | 10 |
|---|---|---|---|---|---|---|---|---|---|
| 11 | 12 | 13 | 14 | 15 | 16 | 17 | 18 | 19 | 20 |
| 21 | 22 | 23 | 24 | 25 | 26 | 27 | 28 | 29 | 30 |
| 31 | 32 | 33 | 34 | 35 | 36 | 37 | 38 | 39 | 40 |
| 41 | 42 | 43 | 44 | 45 | 46 | 47 | 48 | 49 | 50 |
| 51 | 52 | 53 | 54 | 55 | 56 | 57 | 58 | 59 | 60 |
| 61 | 62 | 63 | 64 | 65 | 66 | 67 | 68 | 69 | 70 |
| 71 | 72 | 73 | 74 | 75 | 76 | 77 | 78 | 79 | 80 |
| 81 | 82 | 83 | 84 | 85 | 86 | 87 | 88 | 89 | 90 |
| 91 | 92 | 93 | 94 | 95 | 96 | 97 | 98 | 99 | 100 |

**3** If you found a 5c coin every day for 5 days, how much money would you have? Use the 100 square to help you.

**Answer:**

**Marks:** /3



**Today's Marks:** /6

## Day Four Try these.

**Top Tip!**

We can use a frame ☐ to help us understand an unknown number.

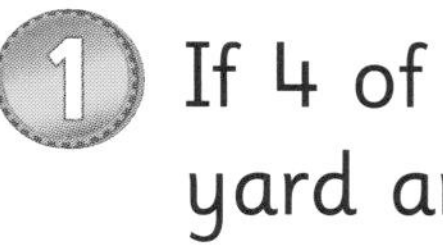

**Team Talk**

Reader
Calculator
Checker
Reporter

1. If 4 of my friends are playing a game in the yard and 5 more girls join, how many will be playing the game?

**4 + 5 = ☐**

Marks: ☐ /1

2. Layla read a total of 10 books over the summer holidays. If she read 4 in July, how many did she read in August?

**4 + ☐ = 10**

Marks: ☐ /2

3. There were 6 potatoes left over in the pot after dinner. 8 potatoes were eaten during dinner. How many potatoes were in the pot to begin with?

**☐ – 8 = 6**

Marks: ☐ /3

Today's Marks: ☐ /6

## Super Sleuth investigates

1. What patterns can you find in the image?
2. How many different patterns of circles are there?

**Joke!**

Which snakes are good at maths?
Adders!

Total Marks: ☐ /21

Got this!  Getting there.  Need help! 

I enjoyed ☐

# 27  3-D Shapes

**We are learning to:** Name 3-D shapes, including cube, cuboid, cylinder and sphere. ☐ Describe and compare 3-D shapes. ☐ Explore the relationship between 2-D and 3-D shapes. ☐

## Day One Look at the example below.

What 2-D shape is each face of a cube?

CLUES

**Circle the numbers and keywords:** 2-D shape, cube

**Link with operation needed (+ or –):** None

**Use a strategy:** Patterns

| **Estimate and calculate:** My estimate: a flat face | Each face of a cube is square. | **Answer:** a square |
|---|---|---|

**Summarise how you got your answer:** I know that a cube has 6 square faces.

### Try these.

CLUES

1. Name the shapes that can roll. Explain why they can roll.

Marks: /1

2. Name the shapes that can slide. Explain why they can slide.

Marks: /2

3. Name the shapes that can stack. Explain why they can stack.

s
t
a
c
k

Marks: /3



Today's Marks: /6

## Day Two Try these.

These shapes broke into a farmer's field to play! Super Sleuth is on the case, investigating the muddy prints that they left on the road.

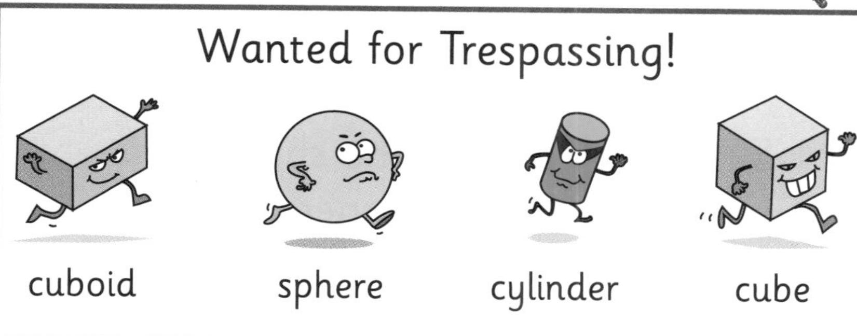


1. Which 3-D shape could have left this muddy print?

| Answer: | | Marks: | | /1 |
|---|---|---|---|---|

2. Which 3-D shape could have left this muddy print?

| Answer: | | Marks: | | /1 |
|---|---|---|---|---|

3. Which 3-D shape could have left this muddy trail?

| Answer: | | Marks: | | /2 |
|---|---|---|---|---|

4. Do you think that the same print would be left by each shape if it turned itself on its side? Explain your answer.

### Super Sleuth investigates

Gather a collection of 3-D shapes and use sand or modelling clay to investigate the print that each one makes. You could also use paint and turn your prints into a work of art.

**Deeper investigation:**

Can any of the 3-D shapes make more than one kind of print?

## Day Three Try these.

1. Eleanor baked two cakes for her twin nephews' birthday. She baked a Spider-Man cake in the shape of a cuboid and a Superman cake in the shape of a cube. How many corners did the two cakes have altogether?

Answer: Marks: /1

2. Thomas baked two caterpillar cakes using cylindrical (cylinder-shaped) cake tins. How many edges did the cakes have in total?

Answer: Marks: /1

3. Liam's birthday cake showed the Solar System. How many curved faces, edges and corners were there on the sun and the 9 planets in total?

Answer: Marks: /2

4. Trish loves Thor and wants her birthday cake to be in the shape of a hammer. Her daddy plans to bake the hammer cake using two cake tins of different shapes. The tins have **14** edges in total. What shapes are they?

Answer: Marks: /3



Today's Marks: /7

## Day Four Try these.

Using the clues below, change these 3-D shapes into real-life objects. Draw on or colour the shapes to make them realistic. Try your best!

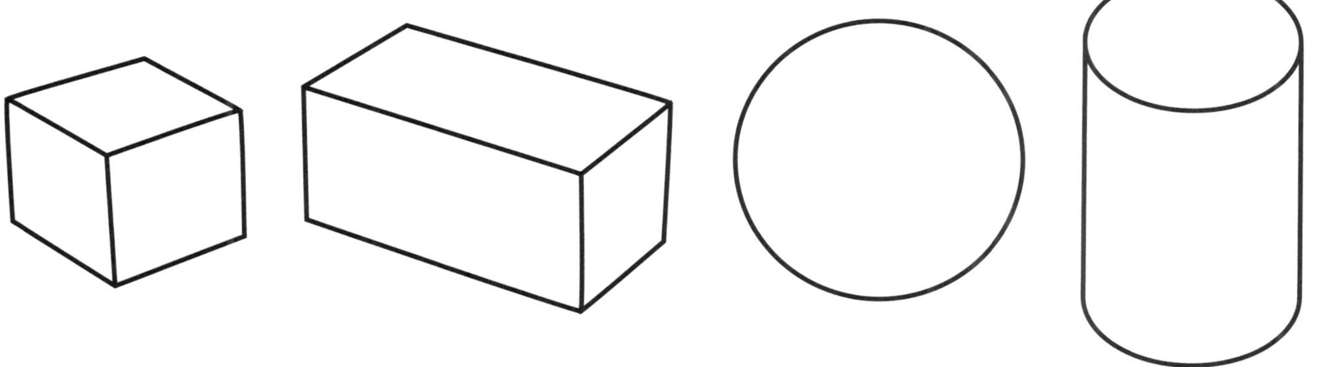

1. The cylinder becomes a tin of soup. **Marks:** /1
2. The cube becomes a wrapped present with a bow on top. **Marks:** /1
3. The cuboid becomes a block of butter. **Marks:** /2
4. The sphere becomes a basketball. **Marks:** /3

**Today's Marks:** /7

## Super Sleuth investigates

1. What 3-D shapes can you identify?
2. Find a blue shape. What 2-D shape is each of its faces?

**Total Marks:** /27

Got this!  Getting there.  Need help! 

My favourite activity was

# 28 Operations 2

**We are learning to:** Add numbers, without and with renaming, within 99. ☐ Estimate differences within 99. ☐ Explore and discuss repeated addition and group counting. ☐ Subtract numbers, without renaming, within 99. ☐

## Day One Look at the example below.

Miss Carroll went to the art shop to buy a set of 28 small aprons and a set of 28 large aprons. How many aprons did she buy?

**C**ircle the numbers and keywords: 28, 28, how many?

**L**ink with operation needed (+ or –): Add (+).

**U**se a strategy: Draw a picture.

**E**stimate and calculate:

My estimate: more than 40

| T | U |
|---|---|
| 2 | 8 |
| +2 | 8 |
| 5 | 6 |

**Answer:** 56

**S**ummarise how you got your answer: I added 2 groups of 28.

### Try these.

CLUES

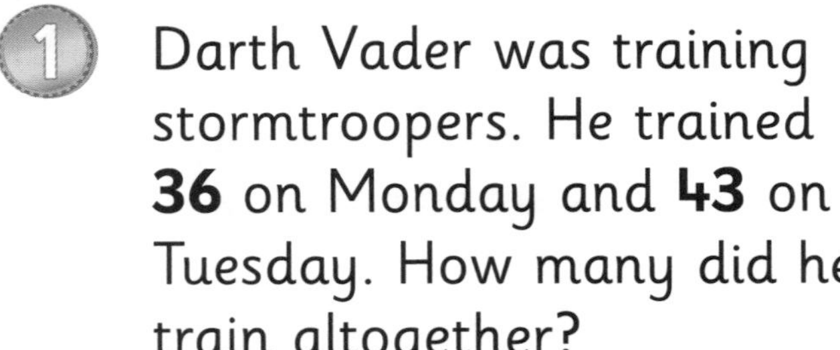

1. Darth Vader was training stormtroopers. He trained **36** on Monday and **43** on Tuesday. How many did he train altogether?

| T | U |
|---|---|
| | |
| | |

Marks: /1

2. The Darth Vader Interactive Figure costs **€49**. How much would it cost for two of them?

| T | U |
|---|---|
| | |
| | |

Marks: /2

## Puzzle Power

What belongs to you, but others use it more than you do?

| 12 | 10 | 5 | 7 | 15 | 8 | 20 |
|---|---|---|---|---|---|---|
| s | a | e | t | m | i | n |

| 12 + 8 | 7 + 3 | 8 + 7 | 3 + 2 |
|---|---|---|---|
| = | = | = | = |

Today's Marks: /3

## Day Two Try these.

CLUES

**Team Talk**

Reader

Calculator

Checker

Reporter

1. There are **52** Lego bricks in a box. How many more are needed to make a boat using **75** bricks?

52

| T | U |
|---|---|
| | |
| | |

**Marks:** /1

2. Katrina had a tub of **98** Lego bricks in her bedroom. If **64** of them were large bricks, how many small bricks did she have?

| T | U |
|---|---|
| | |
| | |

**Marks:** /1

3. Zara wants to buy a Lego Friends set that costs **€25**. She has saved up **€59**. How much money will she have left?

Lego Friends

LEGO

| T | U |
|---|---|
| | |
| | |

**Marks:** /2

4. **60** Lego storage boxes were delivered to a toy shop on Monday. **23** were sold on Tuesday and **11** were sold on Wednesday. How many were left?

| T | U |
|---|---|
| | |
| | |

| T | U |
|---|---|
| | |
| | |

**Marks:** /3

## Day Three Try these.

Top Tip! Simplify.

Which symbol (+ or –) is needed for each of the following number stories?

1. Denise has baked **68** buns for a cake sale. If she promised to donate **99** buns in total, how many more will she bake?

Answer: | Marks: /1

2. Symon made **46** napkin swans for a wedding. His brother Stefan made a further **35**. How many napkin swans were there altogether?

Answer: | Marks: /1

3. There were **75** children at the cinema. **33** were in Screen 1 and the others were in Screen 2. How many children were in Screen 2?

Answer: | Marks: /2

4. Michele made **38** lattes in the morning and **56** lattes in the afternoon. How many did she make in total?

Answer: | Marks: /3

### Puzzle power

Complete the grid by adding the two previous numbers in each row.

| 1 | 3 | 4 | 7 | 11 |
|---|---|---|---|---|
| 10 | 12 | | | |
| 20 | 10 | | | |
| 16 | 9 | | | |



Today's Marks: /7

## Day Four Try these.

CLUES

1. Arrange the digits **1**, **2**, **3** and **4** in the squares so that the sum is correct. Can you think of a number story?

$$\begin{array}{r} \square\square \\ -\ \square\square \\ \hline 2\ 2 \end{array}$$

Marks: /1

2. Using the digits **5**, **6**, **7** and **8**, subtract the **smallest** two-digit number that you can make from the **largest** two-digit number that you can make.

$$\begin{array}{r} \square\square \\ -\ \square\square \\ \hline \end{array}$$

Marks: /2

3. Think of the smallest two-digit, **even** number that it is possible to make. Subtract this number from the largest two-digit, **odd** number that it is possible to make.

$$\begin{array}{r} \square\square \\ -\ \square\square \\ \hline \end{array}$$

Marks: /3

Today's Marks: /6

## Super Sleuth challenge

Take turns rolling a pair of dice. Player A is **minus** and player B is **plus**. Start at 14 and subtract/add your score each time. If the counter goes down to 1, **minus** wins and if it goes up to 27, **plus** wins.

1 2 3 4 5 6 7 8 9 10 11 12 13 14 15 16 17 18 19 20 21 22 23 24 25 26 27

Total Marks: /23

Got this! Getting there. Need help!

I helped my friend by

# 29 Revision 5

## Minecraft

## Day One Try these.

1. Colour the glasses in this order: full, nearly full, nearly empty.

Top Tip!
Act it out.

Marks: /1

2. The bottle holds **1** litre and the bucket holds **6** litres. How many bottles of water will it take to fill the bucket?

Answer: Marks: /1

3. The Minecraft police cars need oil to run properly. Each car needs **2** litres. How many litres are needed for **3** cars?

Answer: Marks: /2

4. Steve needs **14** litres of paint to paint a building. If he has **9** litres, how many more does he need?

Answer: Marks: /3


Strand: Measures Strand Unit: Capacity
Strand: Algebra Strand Unit: Extending and Using Patterns
Strand: Shape and Space Strand Unit: 3-D Shapes Strand: Number Strand Unit: Operations

Today's Marks: /7

## Day Two Try these.

CLUES

| 1 | 2 | 3 | 4 | 5 | 6 |
|---|---|---|---|---|---|
| 7 | 8 | 9 | 10 | 11 | 12 |
| 13 | 14 | 15 | 16 | 17 | 18 |
| 19 | 20 | 21 | 22 | 23 | 24 |
| 25 | 26 | 27 | 28 | 29 | 30 |

1. Look at the number chart above. Colour all of the **odd** numbers **less than 10** yellow. How many are there?

| Answer: | | Marks: | | /1 |
|---|---|---|---|---|

2. Look at the number chart above. Colour all of the **even** numbers **10 or more** red. How many are there?

| Answer: | | Marks: | | /1 |
|---|---|---|---|---|

3. If the pattern below was repeated 3 times, how many Enderman blocks would there be?

| Answer: | | Marks: | | /2 |
|---|---|---|---|---|

4. Harry played Minecraft for **5** nights and scored **20** points each night. How many points did he score altogether?

| Answer: | | Marks: | | /3 |
|---|---|---|---|---|

# Day Three Try these.

1 Can the Minecraft Pokéball roll, slide or stack?

**Top Tip!** Act it out.

**Answer:** | **Marks:** /1

2 What 2-D shapes do a cube and a cuboid have?

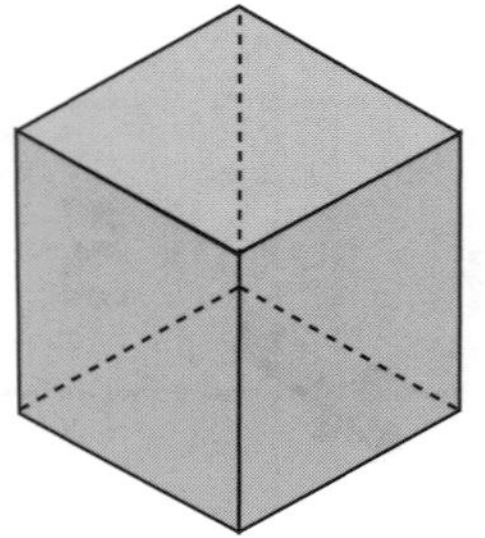

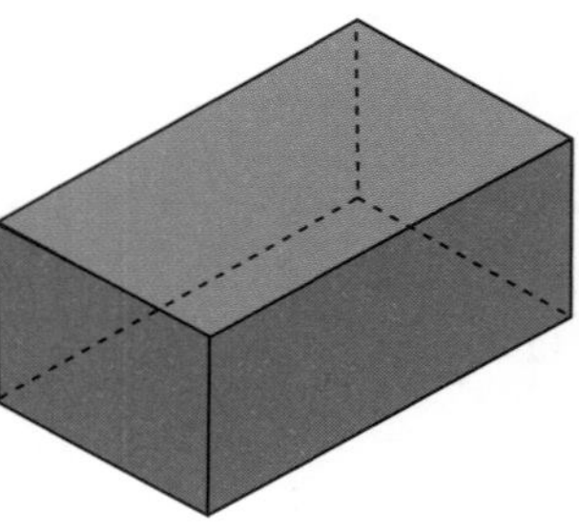

**Answer:**

**Marks:** /1

3 What 3-D shapes were used to create this Minecraft piece? Tick (✓) the correct answers:

cube

cuboid

cylinder

sphere

**Marks:** /2

4 How many **(a)** cuboids and **(b)** cubes can you count in this image?

**Answers:** (a) (b) | **Marks:** /3



**Today's Marks:** /7

## Day Four Try these.

1. **24** zombies and **32** creepers are ready for battle. How many zombies and creepers are there altogether?

| Answer: | | Marks: | | /1 |
|---|---|---|---|---|

2. Rachel scored **65** points and Sally scored **15** less than her. How many points did Sally score?

| Answer: | | Marks: | | /2 |
|---|---|---|---|---|

3. Steve's new house has **25** windows. He wants to add **13** more windows at the back of the house and remove **10** from the front. How many windows will he have then?

| Answer: | | Marks: | | /3 |
|---|---|---|---|---|

Today's Marks: /6

## Super Sleuth challenge

Roll a pair of dice. Colour the sum of the two numbers. Keep rolling the dice until you have completed the picture.

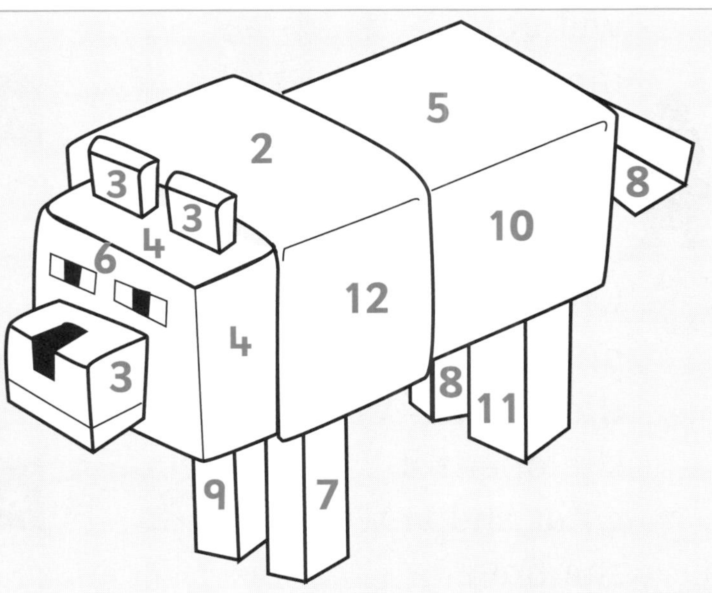

**Joke!**

Why did the teacher write the maths problem on the window?
He wanted it to be very clear!

Week 30

# 30 Strategy: Make a Model

## Day One

Making a model of a number story can help you to picture the puzzle in your mind and figure it out more easily.

**Try these.**

1. Larry has 5 cubes. Can you think of any capital letters that he could make? Draw them.

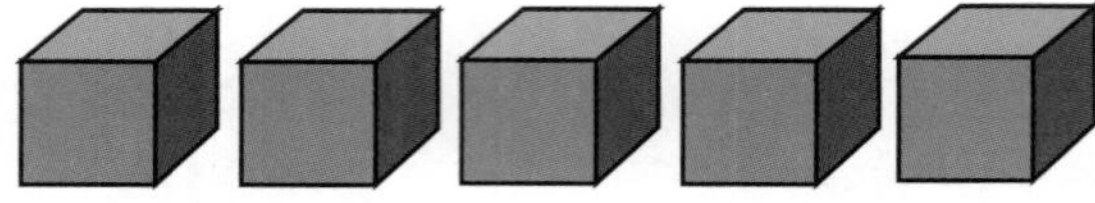

Answer:

Marks: /1

2. I have 12 equal-sized squares. How many 3-D shapes can I make?

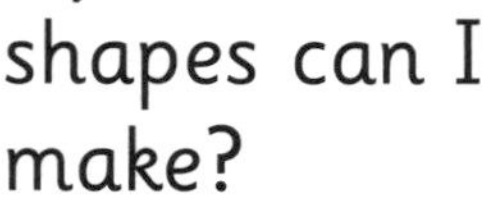

Answer: Marks: /1

3. If you stack some €1 coins, what 3-D shape will you make?

What 3-D shape is one €1 coin? Think about it!

Answer:

Marks: /2

4. Chloë folded a piece of paper in half and cut out the middle. When she opens it, what shape will she have?

Answer:

Marks: /3



Today's Marks: /7

## Day Two Try these.

**Team Talk**

- Reader
- Calculator
- Checker
- Reporter

1. Count how many Play-Doh spheres were made to fill this plate. How many would you need to fill 2 similar plates?

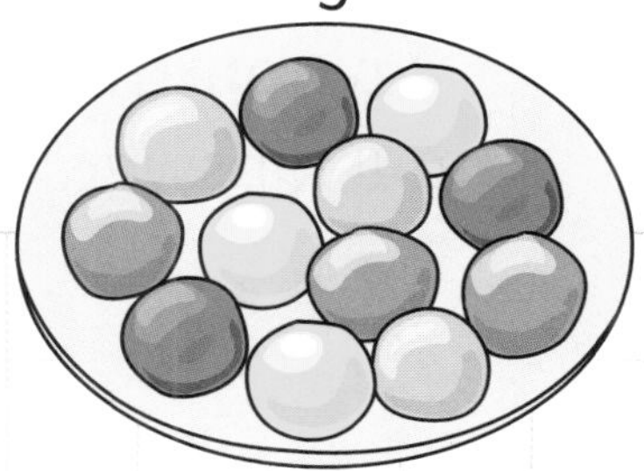

| Answer: | | Marks: | /1 |
|---|---|---|---|

2. How many straws in total would you need to make a triangle and a square?

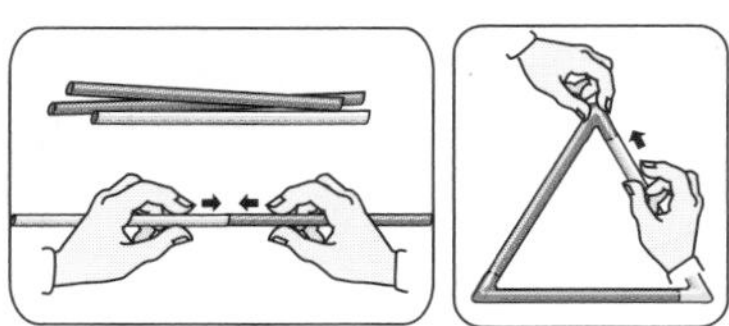

| Answer: | | Marks: | /1 |
|---|---|---|---|

3. How many **(a)** cocktail sticks and **(b)** mini marshmallows does it take to make a cube?

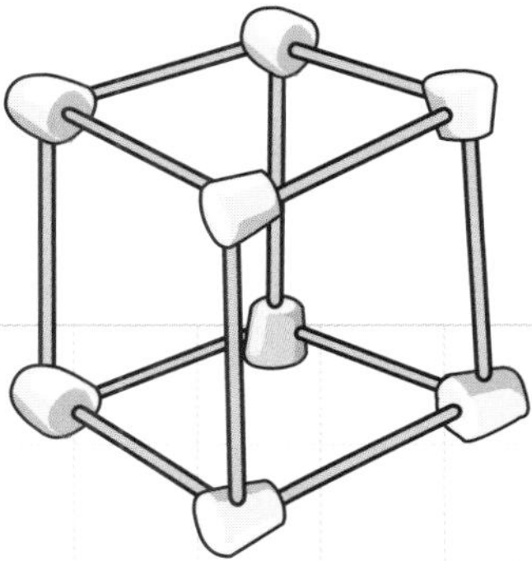

| Answers: | (a) | (b) | Marks: | /2 |
|---|---|---|---|---|

4. Find two unifix cubes and join them together. Look at the shape you have made. Does it have any more corners, faces or edges than one unifix cube? Explain.

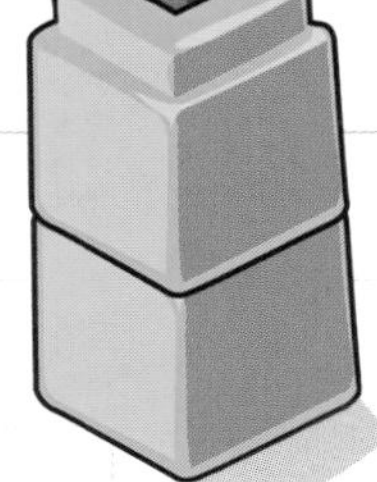

| Answer: | | Marks: | /3 |
|---|---|---|---|

**Today's Marks: /7**

## Day Three Try these.

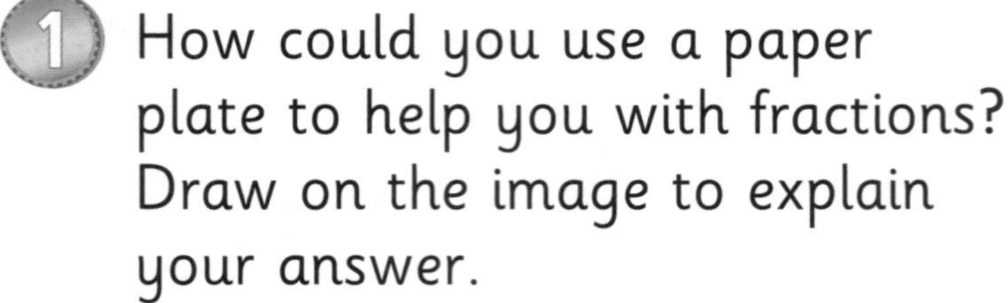

1. How could you use a paper plate to help you with fractions? Draw on the image to explain your answer.

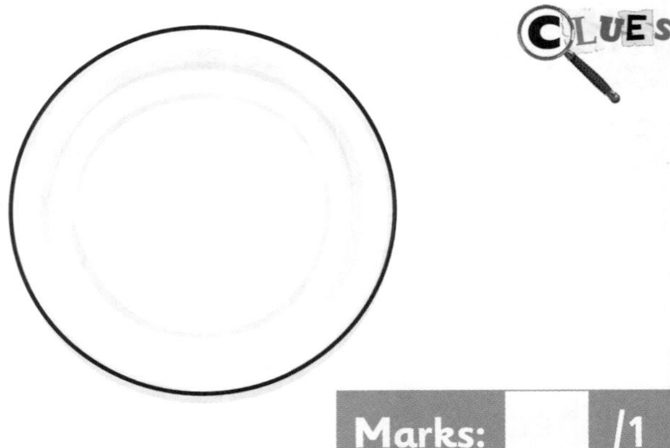


Marks: /1

2. Tammy painted a paper plate to explain time on a clock face. Which do you think she wanted to explain: o'clock or half past?

Answer: Marks: /1

3. 1st Class made a model of a clock face. Look at the amount of unifix cubes that they placed between each number. What is the pattern?

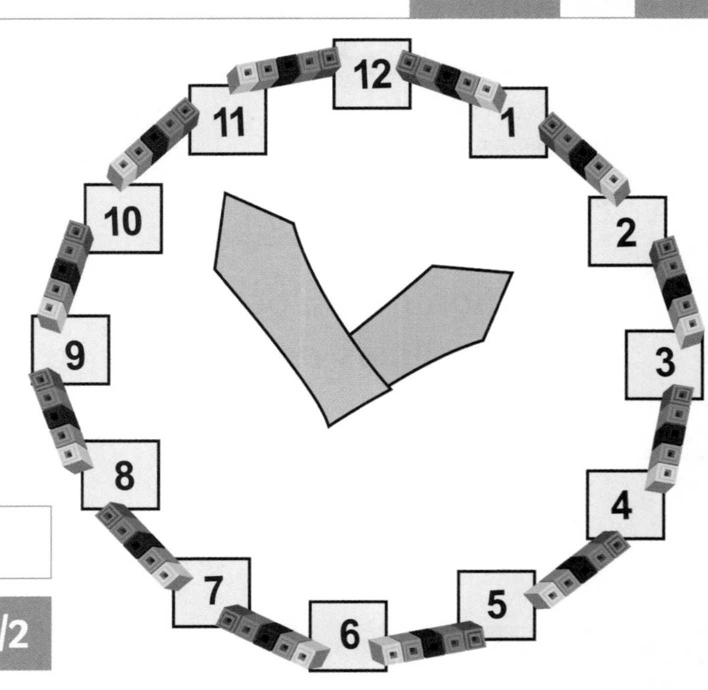


Answer:

Marks: /2

4. Look at the image. What number comes next in the sequence?

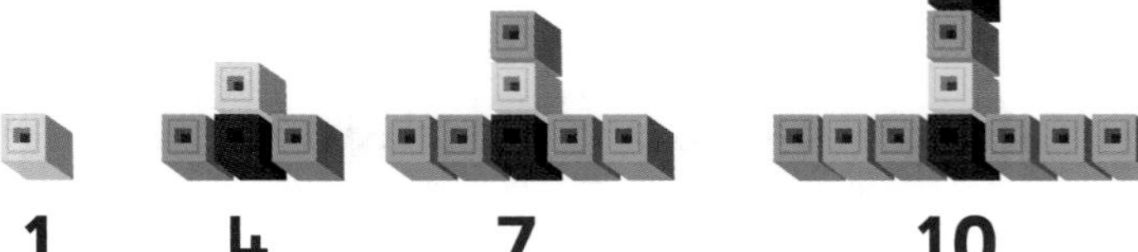


Answer: Marks: /3



Today's Marks: /7

## Day Four Try these.

1. Olivia has made a graph using toys. What do you think her graph is explaining? Tick (✓) the correct answer.

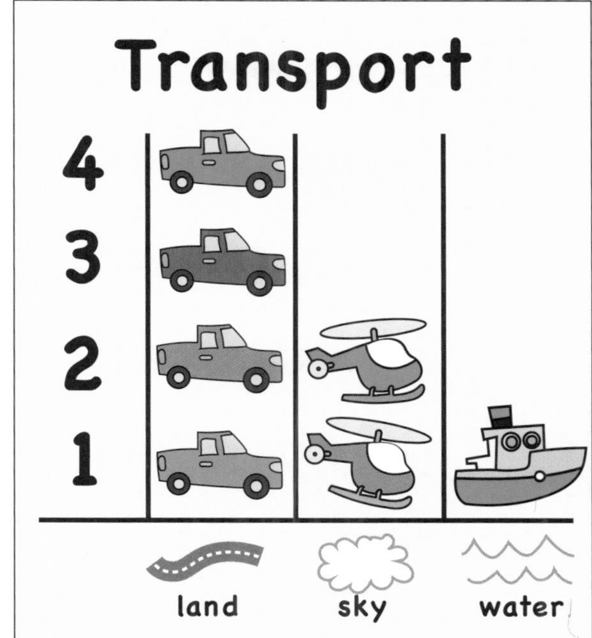


Fun toys for bathtime

Different ways of travelling

A new kind of carpark

Marks: /1

2. What two-digit number is Josh making with the paper cups?

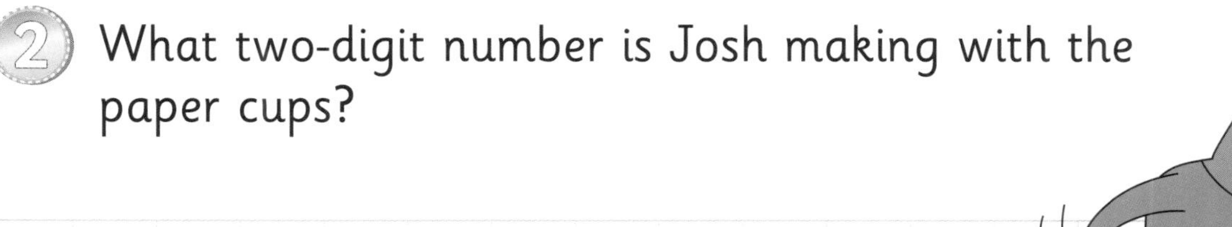

Answer: Marks: /2

3. Casey has made a place value abacus using string and beads. What is the value of **(a)** the string of **blue** beads and **(b)** the string of **green** beads? **(c)** What number has she made?

Answers: (a) (b) (c) Marks: /3

Today's Marks: /6

Total Marks: /27 Got this!  Getting there.  Need help! 

I loved doing